PRAISE FOR
CAN'T TAME A MONGOOSE

"People like Stan Rose were instrumental in making the genomic revolution happen, but technology alone would not have been sufficient without the drive, passion, and determination that Stan so clearly illustrates in *Can't Tame a Mongoose*. A must read for anybody that thinks a great idea is all you need to be successful."

— Riccardo Pigliucci, technology executive/board member

"The vast majority of technology-based start-ups don't survive five years. Stan Rose uses personal stories to illustrate how unexpected events—and the inability of leaders to be prepared to address them—contribute to this high failure rate. Stan also shares values and skills that enhance the likelihood of successfully navigating such events. Aspiring entrepreneurs, early-stage executives, and investors would benefit from reading this book."

— Sue Siegel, chairman of the board of The Engine,
   built by MIT, where she is a sr. lecturer at the
   Sloan School of Management; Board of Directors:
   Align Technologies, Illumina, Nevro, KFF

"Anyone considering investing in a young company developing a 'leapfrog' technology for an existing market should read *Can't Tame a Mongoose*. Stan's real-life story of overcoming technical, financial, and competitive hurdles shows how the right responses in dire situations can make or break the business. As an investor in Stan's start-ups, I have watched him raise money in very difficult venture financing markets, prevail in the face of cutthroat marketing by established large competitors, and build very successful companies."

—L. Robert Johnson, Founders Capital Partners

"A well-written, insightful, and from-the-heart account by an extraordinary scientist and entrepreneur. By sharing his life experience with candor and clarity, Stan Rose will inspire and energize a new generation of thinkers to leverage their intellectual and pragmatic talents to our collective greater good."

—Lena Chow, founder and president of Bob's Last
   Marathon Foundation and City of Paris, Inc.

"A thoughtfully written account, by a successful serial entrepreneur in the genomics space, of a palpable real-life experience with a focus on dealing with uncertainties and unexpected turns. A treasure trove of lessons learned, and practical insights."

—Michael Abecassis, MD, MBA, surgeon, scientist,
   and cofounder of Transplant Genomics Inc.

"I worked with Stan closely on his Transplant Genomics business build. He is a mission-driven leader with incredible savvy to navigate the ups and downs of the entrepreneurial and genomics world. He has so much to offer. This is an essential read for any entrepreneur, investor, or executive."

—Rob Webb, healthcare investor

"Stan Rose has a long track record of recruiting and working with diverse groups of people around the world, always considering ethics when making difficult decisions, and refusing to work with certain groups or people whom he felt did not adhere to a similar approach. In *Can't Tame a Mongoose*, he illustrates the trials, tribulations, and successes encountered along this thrilling journey. His most important message is that in life and in business one must expect the unexpected. One needs to be aware of the possibility of unexpected events occurring and should plan accordingly to overcome such challenges."

—M. Roy First, MD, former president
   of American Society of Transplantation

"This story is about passion, persistence, adaptability, and an insatiable curiosity—in science, in foreign culture, or in new markets. Fascinating!"

—Manfred W. Baier, PhD, biotechnology
   and business expert in diagnostics

"It may be true that you cannot tame a mongoose, but with the right skills and incentives you can train one. In his insightful look at the business of science, Stan Rose subtly demonstrates how combining outstanding scientific and people skills with a wonderful sense of humor and deep personal integrity can inspire many a mongoose to use its aggressive instincts to build visionary and socially beneficial enterprises."

—Thomas Palay, JD, PhD, cofounder of NimbleGen
Systems and Cellular Dynamics International

"Over 90 percent of technology-based companies fail within five years. Of those that succeed, most must overcome obstacles they never imagined they'd face. Stan Rose shares stories of real-life experiences in the emerging field of bio-technology, providing valuable lessons for navigating such 'inevitable unexpected events.' Anyone who aspires to be a bio or tech entrepreneur would benefit from reading his book."

—Robert Palay, entrepreneur, investor, and
cofounder of NimbleGen Systems and
Cellular Dynamics International

CAN'T TAME A MONGOOSE

CAN'T TAME A MONGOOSE

MEMOIR
of a GENOMICS
ENTREPRENEUR

STAN ROSE, PhD

MILES
POND
PRESS

Disclaimer

This book is a memoir. It reflects the author's present recollections of experiences over time. Some names and identifying details have been changed to protect the privacy of individuals. Some locations, characteristics, and the nature of events have been changed; some events have been compressed; and some dialogue has been re-created or paraphrased to the best of the author's recollection. The author's intent is to share stories based on true events that convey messages relevant to aspiring entrepreneurs and not to disparage, offend, or misrepresent the actions of any person. Throughout this book there are technical terms, financial terms, and acronyms that may have meaning only to those with experience in the relevant field. Lay readers should still be able to follow each story and understand the key messages even if such terms are not understood.

Published by Miles Pond Press, Falmouth, Massachusetts
www.roseventures.net

Edited and designed by Girl Friday Productions
www.girlfridayproductions.com

Cover design: Paul Barrett
Project management: Mari Kesselring
Editorial production: Katherine Richards
Image credits: cover © Shutterstock/TRONIN ANDREI, Shutterstock/Mad Dog

ISBN (hardcover): 979-8-9886112-1-9
ISBN (paperback): 979-8-9886112-0-2
ISBN (ebook): 979-8-9886112-2-6

Library of Congress Control Number: 2023921965

First edition

To Elise, without whose love, support, and encouragement I would never have experienced many of the stories in this book or written them to share with others.

To my living kidney donors, Darren Lee and Ellen Miller, who had the courage and generosity to provide me with the gift of life, for which I am eternally grateful.

In loving memory of Dad and Burke.

What we know about the future is poor;
things that look bad can be the greatest
    luck and vice versa;
sometimes you have to take a chance.

—Paul Rose (1948)

CONTENTS

PREFACE

Can't tame a mongoose.

—West Indian expression, via Jeff James (2004)

Over a fifteen-year period I regularly took taxi rides between the airport in Charlotte Amalie, in the US Virgin Islands, and the ferry dock in Red Hook. Typically I would drive with Jeff James, a good friend who was born on the island of Dominica. We'd pass the time talking about everything under the sun, from local politics or quirky tourist stories to the Yankees-Braves baseball rivalry to global events. One day I went off on a long rant about a certain politician who continually pushed their agenda regardless of what others said. Without taking his eyes off the windy mountain road, Jeff said, "You know what they say, my friend. Can't tame a mongoose."

At first I thought it simply meant that some things are beyond your control, so don't fret over it and move on. On further reflection, I realized that it could also mean that some people will push relentlessly until they get what they want, with the persistence you see in a mongoose chasing a snake. They can't be tamed and will try everything possible to achieve their goal. I believe this same kind of persistence is key to success in business. Especially when attempting to navigate past unexpected events, one must focus intensely, think creatively, rely on relationships, leverage any legitimate ethical advantage, and do whatever it takes to achieve a goal.

INTRODUCTION

Our world is unimaginably complex and beautiful. In biological systems this complexity reveals itself in its near-infinite variation in living organisms and the continual creation of unpredictable new variants. Similarly, every business is unique, every interaction between two companies idiosyncratic. Situations occur routinely that no one could have anticipated. If a fundamental truth exists, it is that much about life remains unknown and the future is difficult to predict. It's thus beneficial to have a healthy respect for things we don't yet know, understand, or expect.

My career has evolved at the crossroads of biology and business, and this memoir intertwines both subjects. I write with aspiring entrepreneurs in mind, although I hope my stories will be appreciated by anyone interested in DNA, genomics, the business of science, or entrepreneurship more generally. These stories primarily comprise companies that commercialized novel analytical tools that enabled scientists to decipher DNA, explore genomes, and make some of the most important advances and discoveries in the life sciences over the past four decades. There are also stories of the personal and professional challenges and opportunities faced by the people who led these businesses, the unexpected events they encountered in their journeys, and how they responded in moments of truth.

New technical ventures are risky. As many as 90 percent of them fail during their first five years. Aspiring entrepreneurs should expect no guarantee of reward in any sense of that word. After working hard for years, your equity could be worthless, and you could find yourself on the street unemployed with a bankruptcy on your résumé. In such environments it helps to be optimistic by nature and passionate about one's goals.

Business schools, venture accelerators, and industry experts have spent considerable effort trying to educate students, founders, and others in new technical ventures about the most frequent causes of failure: lack of product-market fit, marketing problems, team problems, finance problems, technology problems, operations problems, and legal problems. These problems are bad enough, worse when they occur without warning.

As a genomics entrepreneur I've succeeded more frequently than most. I believe this was partly due to a pursuit of opportunities I found intellectually stimulating, with products that offered compelling benefits to meaningfully large markets whose needs I understood. I had developed a strong foundation in my field and was fortunate to find great mentors and partners along the way. I developed close relationships with key opinion leaders, too, and often my partners and I quickly recognized the advantages of new technologies we believed would interest customers. This foresight repeatedly enabled our early entrance into emerging markets. The teams I assembled included highly motivated people with diverse backgrounds and complementary skill sets. We tried to create environments where everyone could thrive.

All this was necessary for success but not sufficient. If I learned anything while becoming a serial entrepreneur, it was this: beware of life's inevitable unexpected events. How leaders respond to unforeseen events determines a business's success or failure. As Louis Pasteur famously noted in 1854, "Chance favors only the prepared mind." I'm convinced that such an adaptive mindset has been one of my most valuable assets.

Based on my three decades in the emerging fields of DNA and genome analysis, I believe there are values, skills, and approaches that, if practiced satisfactorily, can provide strategic advantages and increase the likelihood of success when encountering the unanticipated. I'm not referring to magic bullets or simple formulas but rather a way of thinking and behaving.

The stories in this book occurred during an era of dramatic growth in the genomics industry, mostly between 1980 and 2020. Major advances were achieved in our collective understanding of the structure, function, and regulation of genes and genomes, and in turn biological systems. A new industry based on DNA and genome analysis took off during these years and has never looked back.

A new wave of bioentrepreneurs emerged, motivated by the opportunity to advance science and to translate those advances into commercially available products that improve lives. These new business leaders took great personal risk. They bet on not only the viability of a new technology or product but also their ability to raise money, develop products that customers desired, and effectively execute in every functional area of a business, regardless of what surprises life had in store.

During my career I founded or led businesses that collectively created over a billion dollars in shareholder value and introduced products that positively influenced the lives of millions. I didn't invent these breakthrough technologies, and I don't take credit for their immense impact. Working with amazing scientists and clinicians, my role was to build and lead talented teams to commercialize their inventions, and in doing so enable the scientific community to use our products to make new discoveries. It has been a thrilling and personally fulfilling experience, and well worth the hard work and risk.

In the following pages I write about my youth, my early career with established companies, and my later career as a serial entrepreneur. I'll show how my teams and I navigated unexpected events and arrived, more frequently than not, at successful outcomes. I chose these stories to illustrate what I found most helpful when facing critical and unexpected moments of truth. These were moments I came to appreciate.

1

A DAY IN THE LIFE

It was half past seven and already dark outside as I finally hung up the phone. Another call that went much longer than necessary. The days were getting noticeably shorter now, but those guys on the West Coast couldn't care less what time it was out here in Massachusetts. I sat back in my home office chair and took a few slow, deep breaths, just as I had learned in yoga class. These fourteen-hour days were draining, but I was in the thick of it. One side of my brain was saying "You're getting too old for this," but the other side wouldn't let me stop pushing.

I decided to make a run to the grocery store. I knew that if I stopped now, I'd be done for the night. In the car, I randomly picked a CD from the glove compartment and popped it into the Audi's player. It was a bootleg Grateful Dead recording from February 1969. I forwarded to the last song of the set, a slow psychedelic version of the gospel blues song "Death Don't Have No Mercy," by Reverend Gary Davis. At the time of this concert I had just turned thirteen.

The field of genomics hadn't yet existed. The thought that I would one day become a serial genomics entrepreneur was inconceivable.

I pulled into a parking spot at the local Stop & Shop, closed my eyes, and sat for a few minutes to listen through the climax of Garcia's guitar solo. Suddenly my cell phone began ringing, rudely breaking the mood. My caller ID said it was our banker, Tod. I had to take the call. You can never really completely check out when you're the CEO of an early-stage company, especially when you're in the midst of negotiating a deal.

Recent changes in the Medicare approval process to secure reimbursement for complex diagnostic tests had taken us by surprise. We were developing novel diagnostic tests to rule out organ rejection in kidney transplant recipients, with the potential to improve patient care and extend lives. It would take another six to twelve months and cost several million dollars more than we had to generate the new data they now required. We had engaged Tod to help us raise those funds and, simultaneously, explore the possibility of selling our business to a company that shared our vision, had the resources to take our products into the clinic, and appreciated the value of what we had created. This last criterion really meant that they would adequately reward our early investors.

After months of discussion, we were now in a competitive bidding situation with four companies. Normally this would be a good thing, but we didn't yet have a decision from Medicare to cover our tests so couldn't yet show clear evidence that customers would buy our test, and we were running low on cash. We had discussed a variety of possible partnership arrangements involving an immediate infusion of cash, but none provided the value we were seeking. At some point I needed to just get a deal done, and they all knew it. Time was on their side.

If we couldn't find a new source of cash soon, we might have to accept the least unattractive offer we could get. The possibility of letting down my investors, and potentially failing to achieve our goals, created enormous pressure. On a daily basis I was reminded of the thousands of kidney transplant patients who might benefit from our tests, and I was one of them. I thought about my investors, who had put their money and faith in me to get us to a successful outcome and now might make poor returns or even lose their money altogether. Many were personal friends, and I seriously wondered if they would ever talk to me again. They certainly wouldn't think as highly of me. I thought about my team members. They had been sold on my vision and left other jobs to join me on this mission, taking a gamble and putting everything they had into it. I thought about my family, and of all the hours I had spent on this project, the stress I had put them through, the time together we had missed.

What I had imagined might be the crowning achievement of my career had the distinct possibility of being a major flop. For more than thirty years now, I had been working with scientists and clinicians, helping them commercialize inventions involving genome analysis. My career paralleled and, in some cases, drove the emergence of a new industry providing the tools used in biotechnology. I had a lifetime of experience dealing with stressful situations, but I was older now, already had multiple accomplishments under my belt, and was literally living on spare parts and borrowed time. My doctors kept urging me to slow down, as did my wife, but there was an internal drive that would not let me stop.

I really needed to pick up the phone. Tod might have a new counteroffer. On the other hand, he might be calling to tell me that we had reached the end of the line and had to make a choice among several inadequate offers. Game over.

"Hey, Tod. I'm in the car. What's up?"

"Hi, Stan. I think I may have found an interesting angle for us. It's a bit unusual, so hear me out."

"Okay, I'm listening."

"One of my other clients has been exploring investments from companies in China, so we've been doing quite a bit of networking with Chinese companies that have a strategic interest in healthcare. A few hours ago I spoke with one group that is not a good fit for my other client, though they might be a good fit for you. They're sitting on a lot of cash, and eager to tap into cutting-edge technologies coming out of the US, specifically in the renal-care space."

We hadn't been thinking about China at all. We hadn't even given much thought to Europe! Unlike many of my prior businesses that had a global view from the start, we were solidly focused on the US market for kidney transplant diagnostics.

I knew the board's knee-jerk reaction would be to not get distracted at this late stage of the game. This company had no relevant operations in the US and would never be the ideal partner to achieve our long-term goals. They might have the money we needed, but they lacked critical infrastructure, reputation, and commercial and regulatory experience. Perhaps they could be a silent investor, but the thought of having to travel to Shanghai to update my new lead investor was not a selling point. What's more, there were ethical concerns in the US transplant community regarding reported organ harvesting from political prisoners. A relationship with a Chinese company might taint our reputation in our key market. For all we knew, they might just steal our technology and then compete with us. Theft of US intellectual property by Chinese companies was daily news, with rumors that President Trump was going to shut the door on Chinese investment in US businesses. We might not even be able to get this investment closed in time. It would be a big risk.

On the other hand, they could easily afford the $5 million we needed, and we might even be able to sell them stock at an increased valuation over our prior round. In addition, they had existing relationships with all the major transplant programs in China. Perhaps we could bundle a distribution agreement into this deal, with guaranteed annual minimum payments. We were never going to sell direct in China anyway. We could pitch this to future investors or acquirers as a value-enhancing event, one that opened up a new market for us.

An opportunity had presented itself, but not without risk. We needed to make a decision. The fate of the company, and our ability to affect patient lives, depended on it being the right one. As Tod shared further details, I began reflecting back on the long road that had led to this point.

2

EARLY EXPERIENCES

BEGINNINGS

I'm not sure when I first came to understand what an entrepreneur was, but I certainly didn't grow up wanting to become one. The word and the concept were both foreign to me. The kids I knew wanted to be doctors, lawyers, teachers, firefighters, or police officers. Some dreamed of becoming professional athletes, musicians, or actors. A few knew they would work their way up in a family business, whether that was a restaurant, landscaping company, or auto shop. Others chose to enlist in the armed forces or join the Peace Corps. Literally nobody in my social circles thought about becoming an investment banker or starting a venture capital–financed business.

As for myself, I don't recall having my sights set on any particular career path. What I did have was a sense of curiosity, creativity, and optimism. As far back as I can remember, I had a drive to succeed and, from a relatively early age, a desire to do something of importance. In retrospect I realize I was privileged from the start in several respects. Though I am a white male American unburdened by severe poverty or disability, these advantages were not guarantees of future success.

Big changes were happening in the world during my formative years. Everywhere you looked leaders were emerging—inspirational politicians, activists, athletes, artists, musicians, scholars, scientists, and doctors recognized for their vision, their personal accomplishments, and the positive impact they had on the lives of others. These were my role models. One day I hoped to help affect people's lives positively, find joy, and make my family proud. That would be truly fulfilling. Pretty ambitious thinking, in retrospect. Fortunately I was naive enough not to realize it.

Though I was born in the Bronx, I spent most of my childhood in a diverse middle-class neighborhood in Greenburgh, New York, a suburb of New York City. Many of our neighbors were similarly from working-class families in which at least one parent had a steady job and had achieved a level of success sufficient to buy a starter home. Our parents were mostly immigrants or first- or second-generation Americans. The neighborhood was filled with children, dogs, and bicycles, and we all played outdoors from the end of school until dark. Every Sunday we drove into the city to visit with my grandmother, who lived on the Upper West Side at 148th and Broadway. While we didn't have a large extended family, every holiday was an excuse for a gathering with aunts, uncles, cousins, and grandparents.

My parents both traced their roots back to European lines of Jewish heritage, although neither had any affinity for formalized religion. They belonged to the New York Society for Ethical Culture, which took the place of religion in my life. While most of my childhood friends went to church or synagogue or didn't practice any religion, we religiously attended Sunday-morning meetings of the Society for Ethical Culture. It was not a typical path to follow, and as a child it was awkward trying to explain it to friends. I understood from a very early age what it meant to be different and got comfortable with that fact. It made me more tolerant and accepting of all types of people, gave me a solid ethical foundation, and instilled within me a strong sense of self-confidence and integrity.

My father was born in Hamburg, Germany, in 1923, in the aftermath of World War I. As Hitler came to power in the early 1930s, my grandparents sent him to a Quaker-run school in the Netherlands. They wanted to protect him from the stigma, emotional toll, and relatively poor education that would come from being mandated to attend all-Jewish schools. Letters my father sent home as a young teenager in the late 1930s make it clear that he had no sense of the tragic events to come.

As the situation deteriorated in 1938, his parents and younger brother left everything behind in Germany and came to America to start a new life. Dad stayed in Holland to continue his education, as it was still considered safe enough there. A year later that was no longer the case. One night, Dad was unexpectedly alerted that the Nazis were preparing to invade and that the school could not guarantee his safety. Without a clear plan, he quickly packed a knapsack and left, bicycling across the Netherlands to Rotterdam, where an uncle lived. A few weeks later, just before the Nazis invaded Holland, Dad's uncle was fortunate enough to get him on a freighter out of Antwerp bound for Hoboken, New Jersey. His schoolmates who stayed behind met their fate in Hitler's concentration camps.

Just a few years later, Dad would enlist in the US Army and be sent to the Pacific theater. He wound up in Tokyo, helping clean up the mess after Allied firebombing left more than one hundred thousand dead and a million homeless. It was a lot to live through by the age of twenty-two.

My mother's grandmother immigrated to the US in the late 1800s from Odessa, Ukraine. From 1881 to 1912, nearly two million Jews immigrated to the US from this region as a result of persecution. The family settled in Connecticut, near Norwich. My mom's father, Alec, or "AJ," had wanted to become a doctor, but that changed suddenly when his father passed away at an early age. Instead, AJ dropped out of college and got a job to support the family. He became a traveling salesman for MGM, distributing movies to theaters all over New England. AJ married, and they had one child before my mom's mother succumbed to cancer in her thirties, unexpectedly making AJ a single father. Thus from an early age I learned many family stories of lives being affected by unanticipated events.

I grew up under more stable circumstances, in a strong, expanding post–World War II economy. My parents tried to create the picture-perfect 1960s household. Dad rode the train into the city for work every day and took the family on vacations at least once a year. Those trips instilled in me a lifelong love of travel and a strong desire to see the world for myself. My mother was a homemaker whose cooking skills didn't go beyond TV dinners. She made up for that deficit by doing all she could to enrich her children's lives, taking us to movies, museums, zoos, and other sites of interest in the New York metro area.

The stability I experienced as a young child would not last long, for either the US or my family. The late '60s and early '70s were turbulent times in America. We lived through the Vietnam War, race riots, protests of all sorts, assassinations (JFK, MLK, RFK), and Watergate. It was also a time of enhanced personal freedoms: the height of the civil rights movement; hippies and the summer of love; rock and roll music and the sexual revolution; women demanding and securing the right to choose what to do with their own bodies. It was an especially exciting time for science. In the 1950s computers had become the next frontier, and by the end of the 1960s Neil Armstrong had set foot on the moon. Every kid growing up in the Sputnik generation wanted to be an astronaut!

I don't recall the desire or pressure to make money for money's sake, but as far back as I can remember, it was simply assumed that one day I would go to college and then pursue a career of some sort. I was ambitious and worked odd jobs from an early age: selling lemonade from a stand, mowing lawns, raking leaves, shoveling driveways, delivering newspapers, caddying at a golf course, unpacking boxes at a grocery store. It felt good to have some pocket change to spend on comic books or candies, and my parents were pleased that I was using my spare time constructively instead of just playing basketball.

During high school, life changed dramatically as my parents' marriage crumbled. Fights were constant. I played peacemaker and tried to protect my two younger sisters, always in the belief that things would eventually settle down. At some point I accepted that it just wasn't meant to be, and indeed my parents divorced during my senior year.

When I was a preteen, my parents began sending me off for a month in the summer to Camp Abelard in the Catskills, a welcome break from the drama at home. The camp was billed as a getaway for inner-city kids, but the population included some children from liberal suburban families who supported the cause. It's still not completely clear to me what that cause was, but I came to learn that Abelard was viewed by some as a breeding ground for young Communists. This wouldn't have been particularly offensive to me, as I was comfortable in very liberal environments. Some might say those at Abelard were enlightened, and others might call them hippies. I'm not sure what my parents were thinking or if they were even aware.

I just had the sense I was spending a summer among well-meaning people who were kind, tolerant, creative, and fun. We did all the things kids did back in those days. We cleaned our bunks, learned various arts and crafts, spent a lot of time hiking and playing softball and swimming in the creek. We had communal meals, concerts, and plays, along with informal music lessons, drama lessons, and pickup basketball games.

I met kids from all over—Harlem, Williamsburg, Flatbush, Newark. We were thrown together, given all sorts of opportunities to have the time of our lives, and were pretty much left on our own to see if we could make it work. Regardless of where we came from or what we looked like, at

Abelard we were all just a bunch of young boys spending a few months together in a cabin, with girls of the same age in the cabin next door. We not only made it work; we thrived.

The experiences shared, the friendships formed, and the new perspectives learned all helped to develop in me a world-view that was broader, richer, and more flexible, tolerant, and open minded. The future me would often be challenged to think for myself, to rapidly figure out how to approach new situations, and to rely on trusted relationships for guidance and support, and Abelard had prepared me. Strong bonds were formed, and once we were old enough, we made the time to nurture these relationships beyond those dreamlike summers.

Back at home I started spending more time away from the house. By the age of thirteen I was independent and comfortably traveled alone into White Plains or even the city by bus and subway. I immersed myself in school, which had always come easy to me. It was fun, or at least the courses that interested me were. With a college-educated environmental engineer for a father and a natural desire to learn, I particularly excelled at math and the sciences. I also enjoyed graphic arts, so much so that by my junior year I was seriously considering becoming an artist rather than pursuing a more conventional career path.

My closest friend was Andy DeBiccari, a fellow I met in seventh grade when his family moved to Greenburgh from the Bronx. Andy's parents were of a liberal mindset similar to that of my parents. People with strong principles and kind hearts but no need for organized religion. His house and family became a refuge when my parents were divorcing. As teenagers we both started exploring things around the same time, from school to sports to politics, as well as sex, drugs, rock and roll, and the broader world around us. We loved learning new things, eating good food, seeing live performances (music, sports, whatever art form), and road-tripping. We shared our high school math award and considered ourselves independent thinkers. At least in our minds, we were cool nerds.

Greenburgh Central was a relatively small and progressive public school district. Most students had grown up together, so many of us experienced grades K–12 alongside one another. I didn't know it at the time, but our school system was one of the first to adopt the Princeton Plan as a means for facilitating racial integration. One key element of this program was to create classrooms that reflected the ethnic diversity of the district. Another was to have students of all ages bus to schools in different parts of the community that varied both ethnically and socioeconomically.

Tensions arose from time to time, but the strong bonds we formed helped us to develop into more tolerant and open-minded adults. Our high school, Woodlands, was known for the diversity of its student population, the quality of its basketball teams, and the high percentage of students that went on to college. Most of our parents believed that a good education was the key to getting ahead. We were also fortunate to have a group of highly talented teachers who inspired us.

After applying and being accepted to a half dozen schools, I chose Cornell University for my undergraduate studies. I couldn't wait to go! An Ivy League school in upstate New York, Cornell was located far enough from home to be "away," yet not too far to visit when I wanted. The campus is one of the world's most beautiful, with its famous gorges, glacial artifacts containing creeks and waterfalls that wind their way down to Cayuga Lake. The state Regents Scholarship I had won in high school helped with tuition.

My first two years of college tuition were covered by the proceeds from selling shares of IBM stock that my grandmother had wisely bought back in the 1950s. I'd wind up cobbling together the rest through a combination of that scholarship, student loans, and part-time jobs. Cornell offered a wide variety of excellent academic programs, which meant it would be relatively easy to move in a new direction if my interests changed. I understood that much about the future is uncertain, so it is always good to have options.

On one of my last nights at home, Andy and I sat outside my house in his car, finishing our beers and sharing a few tokes after a long night out. Andy was headed for MIT, and we both realized it might be a while before we saw each other again. We wondered what the future would hold. Neither of us had wealth generation as a life goal, but our conversation shifted to the record-size contract recently signed by Tom Seaver of the New York Mets. Months earlier the team had agreed to pay Seaver $172,500 to throw a baseball for one year, the most ever paid to a pitcher. We both wondered aloud what one could possibly spend that much money on.

Seeking that kind of wealth seemed unimaginable and almost improper. It wasn't something I aspired to achieve. At that point I just wanted to see the world, have close friendships, and live a life full of interesting and joyful experiences. Hopefully I'd also find some way to leave a positive mark on others and have fun in the process.

><<

SEARCHING FOR DIRECTION

I started in Cornell's engineering school but really had no idea what I wanted to do with my life. I viewed my first two years more as an introduction to new knowledge and experiences and a chance to figure out where my passions truly lay. A two-week internship at Dad's engineering firm over my first winter break convinced me that I didn't really want to pursue that path. I just couldn't imagine myself in a white shirt and tie, sitting at a drafting table all day.

From engineering, I transferred to the math department. Then to experimental psychology. Then to biology. None were totally satisfying, even if all were interesting. I enjoyed learning so much that it seemed as if a career in academia might make the most sense, but by the time I was ready to graduate, I didn't have enough courses in any one area other than psychology to consider graduate school. I also didn't have many attractive job prospects.

One interesting offer I did receive was from the Pentagon, to work on a top secret project involving research on visual perception. While I was intrigued, I also had a few concerns. If I accepted the job I'd have to live a long distance from my girlfriend. I also didn't like their refusal to disclose exactly what I was going to be doing until I got there. Distrust of the government was pretty high in those days. The day before I was supposed to start, I told them I had just been offered a job in Boston I couldn't refuse, at double the salary. So off I went to Boston, with no job, only $200 in the bank, and an open offer to crash at Andy's fraternity house at MIT for the summer. Relieved I'd been true to myself, I was optimistic about the future, come what may.

Some might view my graduating with a degree in psychology and no clear job prospects as a waste of time and money. This would be a mistake. At Cornell I had grown significantly as a person and, perhaps most importantly, had learned how to learn. I now had a degree of discipline, an ability to focus, an openness to new information and alternative perspectives, and an approach to analyzing complex questions and expressing my thoughts well. I learned how to use the many tools available to access knowledge, from libraries to experts and experiences (the internet would come later). I formed relationships and shared experiences that expanded my worldview. Diverse perspectives made me a more thoughtful, open-minded, and understanding person. I'd become better prepared to find and cultivate a fulfilling purpose in life.

That summer I shared with two other fellows a bedroom in Andy's fraternity house for fifty dollars a month. When not submitting job applications, I played a lot of basketball; spent afternoons in the bleachers at Fenway Park; and just hung out on the roof getting stoned, listening to music, chatting with new friends, and working on my tan. I tried to visit my girlfriend at Cornell as frequently as possible. She was a year behind me, so that meant we'd take turns traveling between Boston and Ithaca, or Boston and her parents' home in western Maine.

Unexpectedly, her father became one of my role models. A West Point graduate and former MIT professor, he had tired of the bureaucracy and the academic rat race—which should have been a red flag for me—and bought a two-hundred-acre former farm in western Maine, due east of Mount Washington. He had been consulting as a professor and turned that into a full-time business. He built out an office in his basement and added a sauna in back. He had control over his schedule and would take breaks to go hiking with his wife or play with the kids whenever he pleased. Working from home, in a beautiful location, on his own terms, well enough paid, and doing groundbreaking research that led to inventions that benefited people—a perfect career structure, in my view.

I spent all summer trying to find a research job in a biology laboratory. I needed to see if I really enjoyed it, gain some meaningful experience, and enhance my résumé. Responses to my application letters came slowly, and sometimes I got no reply at all. Other times I was told that the job had been filled or that my qualifications were not the best match. I was invited to several interviews, but something wasn't quite right about the people or the actual job they described.

Then one day I finally received an attractive offer. It involved research in the psychobiology lab at Harvard Medical School, under the direction of Dr. Peter Dews, a contemporary of behavioral psychologist B. F. Skinner. Under Dews's direction the lab was researching a variety of psychoactive drugs and evaluating their effects on memory, perception, and conditioned behavior in animals. My résumé jumped out at them, they said, because I mentioned that drawing was one of my hobbies. Dr. Dews had a separate job opening for an illustrator for manuscripts and posters, and I was able to fill both roles.

Within a few months I realized I enjoyed working in the lab. Clear, too, was my desire to perform experiments of my own design, not just conduct projects conceived by others. For that I needed a PhD. Wanting to stay in the Boston area, and being overconfident or naive or both, I decided to apply only to MIT and Harvard. Dr. Dews offered to write a letter of recommendation and introduce me to colleagues at MIT. At the end of my MIT interview, I was told point-blank that I'd be accepted, so I never even pursued the Harvard application. In September 1979 I enrolled and began working toward my PhD.

Graduate school was eye opening. I spent my first two years consumed with coursework, as well as learning laboratory techniques by assisting others on their projects. While my tuition was covered by grants, I had little extra income on which to live. A job working the weekend graveyard shift as a blood bank technician helped me survive but also contributed to the end of my relationship with my girlfriend.

My idealistic notions of what life would be like in the ivory tower were quickly dispelled. I came to understand the intense internal politics that govern academic laboratories and departments, and unwritten rules of engagement often allowed for bullying, harassment, and discrimination. The quest for tenure depended as much on social interactions and one's ability to raise money as it did on academic accomplishments. Professors were in a rat race of grant funding, publishing preliminary data, and using that data to apply for the next round of grants. Science was getting done, but the context in which it occurred disturbed me. I was not having fun.

Alongside my disenchantment with academia was a

growing fascination with a nascent industry: biotechnology. When I began graduate school, the conventional wisdom among my professors and peers was that industry jobs were the final resting place for losers who couldn't make the cut in academia. Biotech changed all that. There was an unprecedented opportunity to raise big money to pursue large-scale biological research and to transform the results of that research into products that actually affected people's lives. Many of my professors started getting involved in biotech companies. When Genentech—regarded by some as the world's first biotech company—went public on the New York Stock Exchange in October 1980, its stock value soared, and the industry captured the public's imagination.

Over the next two years several key events set me on a new course. My original thesis advisor was denied tenure. Embarrassed and disheartened, he left MIT for a tenure-track position elsewhere. At the same time, I was awarded a National Science Foundation fellowship, which provided funding in my own name, thereby giving me the opportunity to transfer to another lab at MIT and continue my work. With my required coursework complete, I could focus all my attention on my thesis research: investigating the role of 1,25-dihydroxyvitamin D_3 in regulation of pituitary function.

Most importantly, I met my future wife, Elise, who was a fellow graduate student focused on cancer biology. Over a year or so, what started as friendly banter among lab mates led to afternoon outings on the beach at Plum Island, late-night debates at the graduate-student pub, and eventually much more. On the evening of May 4, 1984, having just finished our experiments for the day, we drove north to Salem,

New Hampshire, where we were married by a justice of the peace. Aside from being the love of my life, Elise became and continues to be my most trusted advisor.

With Elise's inspiration, guidance, and support, I came to see the importance of the emerging field of molecular biology, which was foundational to much of biotechnology. She introduced me to DNA analysis, and when I expressed an interest in biotech, she encouraged me to pursue a minor in management at MIT Sloan. I didn't need an MBA as a validating credential, as my MIT PhD sufficiently attested to my capabilities, but the courses completed at Sloan provided an introduction to the world of business.

To my great surprise, everything about new venture creation excited me. I learned at Sloan that if you were going to start a new technical venture, then it was a great advantage to understand the technology upon which that venture was based. The class was filled mostly with engineers and computer scientists. Few aside from me understood anything about biology. I saw an opportunity, and it quickly blossomed into my true passion. I would pursue a career in the emerging biotechnology industry, combining my growing knowledge of molecular biology with what I could learn about planning and creating new businesses.

As my thesis work wound down, I found myself so obsessed with this new world of entrepreneurship that I decided to take a shot at starting a company even before graduating. Elise was working with a postdoc who had invented a new technique for detecting amplified DNA in tumor cells. This technology could have great value for other researchers and could lead to a host of diagnostic applications. Over several months we created a business plan, negotiated an option to an exclusive license to patents owned by MIT, convinced two prominent MIT professors to be scientific advisors, and pitched our plan to several venture capital firms (VCs).

It was an exciting time and a great experience, but I wasn't at all prepared for how badly those first few VC meetings went. I quickly realized that the skills I had learned at Sloan hadn't sufficiently prepared me to raise money in the real world. I had to face the reality that I had no idea what I was doing. I didn't really know how to raise money. What's more, if we had raised money, it would have been a disaster, as I didn't know how to actually operate a business.

I needed to learn more, and there was only one way to do this. I had to complete my PhD as quickly as possible and find a job in the biotech industry, where I could learn how things really worked. I needed to build a stronger foundation before ever again thinking about trying to start a company. This became my new mission in life.

3

DNA PROBES AND RFLPS

BUILDING A FOUNDATION

As a child I recall driving down a highway with my father one night, coming around a bend, and seeing an unimaginably large number of headlights and taillights trailing off as far as the eye could see.

"What are all of these people doing on the road?" I wondered aloud. It must have been around rush hour in the wintertime.

"Most of them are either coming home from work or going to work the evening shift somewhere," Dad replied. "You know, if you think about all of the people in the world, the vast majority of them don't have much in the way of formal education and work at whatever jobs they can get to put food on the table, provide shelter, and enable them to support their families. It's actually a pretty rare and special thing to be able to work at a job you enjoy, pursuing a career that you find exciting and fulfilling."

That comment left a lasting impression on me.

I wanted to get involved in this new biotech industry, but not as a bench scientist or even overseeing a research program. I wanted to pursue a career at the interface of business and science. One in which I could apply my knowledge of both disciplines, think strategically, help companies identify new areas worthy of commercial development, and create and implement business plans. That was something I would enjoy. That would be a career I would find exciting and fulfilling.

I needed to develop more skills directly relevant to the kind of role I wanted to play. Strategic planning and new venture creation were often conducted as a function of business development or marketing departments. An entry-level job might involve developing business intelligence upon which to make recommendations concerning resource allocation, new business operations, acquisition targets, or the creation of entirely new businesses as start-ups. Such information was best obtained through what's known as primary market research.

The career center at Sloan had many useful resources for job searches, but this was still in the days before widespread use of personal computers and networking via the internet. Instead, people relied on personal referrals from mentors, writing or calling human resources departments, and watching the bulletin boards at various strategic locations such as the school's career center or in the biology department. It wasn't unusual to go weeks without a single lead and meanwhile making the rounds every day to ensure you didn't miss an opportunity.

One day at the Sloan career center, I found on a bulletin

board an index card seeking a recent MIT grad with a PhD in biology to work as a biotechnology consultant. The pay was horrible, but not any worse than what I lived on as a grad student, and I wasn't doing this for the money anyway. I applied for the job, was accepted, and upon graduation joined a small boutique consulting firm called Consulting Resources Corporation in Lexington, Massachusetts.

My role was to help the founder build a biotechnology consulting franchise for a host of chemical companies that were former clients of his at Arthur D. Little, one of the biggest consulting firms in the industry. I had absolutely no idea what I was doing but was excited and eager to learn. I got them to agree to give me a relatively lofty title, director of biotechnology consulting, which was to our mutual advantage. It didn't cost the company anything more, and it gave me some personal satisfaction and dignity, especially given my low pay rate. What's more, I gave the firm an MIT PhD in a director's role, which helped them establish their brand. The title also gave me external credibility and access to clients and other contacts who might not be interested in speaking with an entry-level associate.

This was a great lesson about the value of titles. Giving someone an impressive title costs nothing, makes the recipient feel good about their role, and enables them to perform better at their job by providing a higher degree of credibility/status. I've often told employees they could have any title they want as long as it was fairly descriptive of their role, allowed them to perform better at their job, didn't upset relationships with other employees, and avoided legal problems (e.g., a title that makes one an officer of a company).

Our market research essentially comprised two

activities. One involved revealing conclusions of strategic interest by studying government or industry records regarding usage of various chemicals, and analyzing the data in ways that our clients had likely not considered. The other approach involved creating interview guides (essentially lists of questions or topics of interest), calling or meeting with people in the relevant industry, writing down their responses, and then reviewing the collective feedback from a representative sample and consolidating it to provide some sort of consensus opinion. Sometimes this could be very quantitative. For example, inquiring as to how much of a particular chemical was used in a given production operation as well as how many similar operations existed in the country, and extrapolating to an approximation of the total amount of a chemical consumed annually in that particular production activity. This information was extremely valuable to executives at chemical companies trying to make decisions about new projects or simply assessing how well they were performing versus their competitors.

My most memorable experience as a consultant occurred in Kansas City. I'd flown there to pitch our services to the vice president of a prominent chemical company trying to diversify its multibillion-dollar food-and-chemical operation. Consulting Resources' founder had a long-standing relationship with senior executives at this company and had briefed them about our new activities in biotechnology. My job was to follow up on that call, meet in person, scope out a specific project, and close the deal. I expected a warm and friendly reception.

I was to meet Mr. VP for breakfast in the lobby restaurant of the Marriott. I had no idea what he looked like, and this was in the days before cell phones, so you couldn't call. Upon entering the restaurant I surveyed the room. Sitting alone at a corner table was a very large man with a fat, puffy white face, balding, wearing a gray suit and silver wire-rimmed glasses. I walked over and asked if he was in fact Mr. VP. Without even looking up at me, he nodded as he shoveled bacon, eggs, and potatoes into his mouth.

I sat down, told him what a pleasure it was to meet him, and thanked him for setting aside some of his precious time for me. After a few more mouthfuls, he finally looked up, still chewing, and asked me in a quiet yet somewhat annoyed tone, "Why in the world would I want to hire a consultant? What could you possibly tell me about my business that I don't already know? I've been in this business for thirty years." He returned to his food while I tried to maintain my composure and considered this unexpected opening move.

Not only had it been a long trip, but my boss wasn't going to be happy about paying the cost of a flight to Kansas City and an overnight stay for a two-minute meeting that led nowhere. What's more, my initial thought was "You're right. I know nothing about your business." But I couldn't say that. I needed to justify my value to him.

So I let him eat a bit more and get a nice swallow in. "Well, sir, I understand your perspective, and you're probably right," I continued. "There's nothing I can tell you about your business that you don't already know. However, I can likely find out things about your customers and competitors that they would be unwilling to tell you, and that could be of value."

Large established chemical companies were simply not well equipped to handle primary market research with respect to opportunities in biotechnology. Back then, few inside these organizations understood anything about the emerging field or how they might benefit as a supplier or customer. Still fewer had personal contacts at the target companies. I went on to explain this to Mr. VP and offered some examples of new areas being addressed by biotech companies that might represent opportunities or threats for his business.

Having finished breakfast, he wiped his mouth, got up from his chair, stuck his hand out, and said, "Sounds interesting. Send me a specific proposal, and we'll consider it."

I shook his hand and thanked him for his time. Meeting over. I got my foot in the door. Keep calm, and always ask for the order.

FINDING AN OPERATING ROLE

After working for five years to get my PhD, the short-duration projects at Consulting Resources were a refreshing change of pace. In less than a year, however, I started to get the feeling that I had learned all I could at this job. Moreover, I was interested in finding a role with more continuity. A project that I could stick with beyond the concept phase, see through to fruition, and use to gain experience in more aspects of business operations than just market research.

Influenced by my fascination with Elise's work and seeing the types of tools that she and her colleagues were using in their molecular biology research at MIT, I focused my attention on the progress and potential of DNA analysis. Two Boston-area companies had strong commitments to this technology. Both were at the forefront of what I believed would be a new generation of research tools and diagnostic tests based on DNA analysis. In considering both of these companies versus the various biopharma companies pursuing "billion-dollar molecules," I remembered that it was the toolmakers who made the most money during the Yukon gold rush.

I wound up taking a job with Collaborative Research Inc., arguably the first biotechnology company, which had been founded by Dr. Orrie Friedman in 1962 while he was a professor at Brandeis. Orrie got started by synthesizing esoteric chemicals and selling them to other scientists performing molecular biological research. Collaborative Research's early products included various cell growth factors and—eventually and most notably—a chemical used to isolate RNA.

Collaborative had an amazing scientific advisory board including famous biology professors from MIT, Harvard, and Stanford. They were talking about mapping the human genome before such a project existed, the types of information that could be discovered and the applications that could benefit humankind. It was pretty intense stuff. The only thing they really lacked was any kind of commercial leadership related to the new DNA-focused business they were building, which I saw as an enormous opportunity.

I hit it off with Orrie and his management team, as well as the senior staff in the research department, led by Helen Donis-Keller and Gerry Vovis. Helen directed human genetics research, aimed at characterizing disease-causing genes and related diagnostic markers, and Gerry led the yeast genetics R&D programs, focused on the manufacture of recombinant proteins. The scientific advisory board was a particular joy to interact with, especially David Botstein and Ron Davis, who played key roles in the company's genome mapping efforts.

I was always energized and inspired after Collaborative's scientific advisory board meetings. At the time I told many people that I would have paid good money just to sit in the audience and watch this brilliant group of scientists work through state-of-the-art problems in real time. I enjoyed my time at the company immensely, but it was the relationships formed that had more lasting value than any particular products or services we brought to market. The early work of this group would lead to the start of the global Human Genome Project, and I would wind up developing close relationships with many of the key players. My involvement in this area, and the relationships formed, would define my career for years to come.

It's been so long since I've had a physical exam required for employment that I'm not even sure whether they are routinely done anymore. In the mid-1980s, however, this was par for the course. I reported for my preemployment physical with no questions asked, didn't consider it a controversial request, and in any case assumed I was in perfect health. The doctor's office was attached to a single-family home in Lexington, a suburb of Boston, up a flight of stairs in the back. All very clean and comfortable, and not rushed as in the big-city medical centers.

The routine itself is familiar to most. Take off everything

but your underpants and get up on the exam table. Measure blood pressure. Take a look into your ears with that pointy lighted device. Up your nostrils too. Shine a light in your eyes. Follow the moving pen light with your gaze. Up, down, to the right, to the left. Stick out your tongue and say "Aah."

The doctor then put his hands around my neck, as if he were going to choke me, but gently. With his thumbs he felt the contours of my throat and then at some point held steady and said, "Please swallow."

I gulped despite the restriction around my throat.

"Swallow again, please." A bit more feeling around before he announced, "Stan, I'm not quite sure, it's very subtle, but I think I feel something in your thyroid gland. If it's real, it's probably just a cyst, but you should get it checked out by a specialist in the next few months, just to be sure. It's really probably nothing serious, but I wouldn't ignore it."

After the obligatory rectal exam, I was asked to please pee in a cup so they could perform a urinalysis. Then I got dressed and drove home. I took note of his recommendation but wasn't unduly alarmed. I was starting an exciting new job, so there was a lot going on in my head.

A few months later the doctor called and asked if I'd ever had any follow-up testing done on that lump. I had forgotten about it, I said. "Well," he replied, "it's probably nothing to worry about, but just to be safe let me make a referral to an endocrinologist to take a look."

The initial exam involved an ultrasound. A technician lubricated the exterior of my neck with some sort of gel, then slid a handheld instrument over the front of my neck while simultaneously looking at a screen. Unmistakably, there was a nodule approximately one centimeter across. I didn't need to wait for a doctor's analysis, as we could both see the image on the screen.

"Well, there's something there, but nine out of ten times these turn out to be cysts," the technician said comfortingly. No need to be alarmed. "The doctor will give you more definitive feedback, but I'd be surprised if they didn't ask you to schedule a biopsy just to be sure it's nothing serious."

On the one hand, I didn't want to ignore the situation, but on the other hand, I never want to waste energy getting overly concerned about something that may not be a problem. So I scheduled the biopsy for a few weeks later and began immersing myself in my work. It also happened that Elise was going through a particularly challenging time in the lab involving a dispute over lead authorship on a paper. This is a big deal, as it indicates who really did the meaningful work on the project, and in academia, credit and your personal reputation are everything. So we had plenty of other things to think about.

When I went in for the biopsy, I was pretty relaxed and a bit curious as to what they were going to do. The first thing a doctor and technician did was apply a local anesthetic to the front of my neck. Then they pulled out a very, very long needle. Were they really going to stick that thing into my neck? Everything was happening very fast now, so I just closed my eyes and silently repeated to myself, "Whatever happens, it'll all be over in a few minutes."

I was surprised when I didn't feel the needle go in at all. I opened my eyes and had a surreal feeling, as if all this couldn't really be happening. I was aware of the needle in my neck and the fluid being extracted out into the syringe, but there was no pain. In less than a minute they were done, and I let out a sigh of relief. Now I'd have to wait for the pathology results.

A few days later the diagnosis came in. Malignant follicular carcinoma. At thirty years old I had thyroid cancer.

✕✕✕

CANCER AT THIRTY

Now my head was spinning. What's the prognosis? How fast does this thing grow? Does it metastasize? How is it treated? How effective is the treatment? Are there any side effects? How will this change my life? How will it affect my job?

Surely Michael Holick would know the answers. Mike was my PhD thesis advisor and an MD, PhD endocrinologist who practiced at Massachusetts General Hospital (MGH, a.k.a. Man's Greatest Hospital). Just as important, he could connect me with the best people in Boston to treat me.

Not long after I called Mike, he immediately introduced me to Gil Daniels, who was *the* thyroid person at MGH. Dr. Daniels was warm and caring with a great bedside manner. After an initial consult, he rapidly concluded that surgery was the best path forward. No radiation treatment. Just get that tumor out, and the best person for that job was Dr. Chiu-An Wang. One of the leading thyroid surgeons in the country, Dr. Wang was older now and only performing surgery selectively. He was likely overseeing students who actually did the work, as that was common practice, although that's not what I was told before they put me under anesthesia.

Dr. Wang and I met in his MGH office, a large wood-paneled room dotted with a few oil paintings and lined with walnut bookshelves filled with medical texts—a classic Ivy League office. Dr. Wang recommended a partial thyroidectomy rather than a full removal of the thyroid gland, as my tumor was still small with no signs of metastasis. This would leave me with some thyroid function that would be supplemented with daily doses of Synthroid, a synthetic form of thyroid hormone.

There were two schools of thought regarding how to approach this, Dr. Wang went on to explain. Some would opt to take out the whole thyroid. In his opinion, however, the more one cuts, the more one risks making a mistake. He looked at me directly and said firmly in broken English, "I do not believe in prophylactic surgery."

"What kinds of mistakes could be made?" I wondered out loud.

"You could cut the nerves that control your vocal cords and wind up with speech problems for the rest of your life," he said. "Or you could accidentally damage the parathyroid glands, which would create problems with calcium metabolism. That would require testing and treating for the rest of your life."

With the long-needled biopsy still fresh in mind, I asked him where he would make the incision, what the approach would be. He motioned with his hand and forefinger, a gesture that eerily resembled a beheading. Then he explained that they would go in from the anterior side, on the front of the neck.

I asked if I would need a blood transfusion too.

The doctor bristled visibly. "I never need blood."

"Okay. Well, this isn't a matter of whether or not to proceed, but I'm just wondering: What will it look like afterwards? Will I have a big scar?"

He was now losing his patience, as if I had just disrespected him. "I will not mutilate you! I am an artist. You will hardly see it."

Now I felt embarrassed. This guy was the best in the world. I was fortunate to have him even consider doing my surgery, and now here I was, questioning his capabilities.

I sat back in my chair, trying to signal that I meant no disrespect and that we were fine to proceed. "Okay, I just have one more question. Are there any other risks that I haven't asked you about?"

Dr. Wang was silent for a few seconds and seemed to be deep in thought. Then he simply said, "Complications."

I leaned forward. "What kind of complications?"

"Could be many things," the doctor replied. "We prepare you for surgery, you're on a gurney being rolled into the OR, the attendant bumps into a wall, and you fall off the gurney. You break your arm. Complication." Then he broke into a big smile and gave me a reassuring look. "Don't worry, my friend. You are in good hands. I have done this many times before, and you're going to be just fine."

Back at the office, I told my immediate superior, Tom Oesterling, what was going on. I might need to take some time off from work, I told him, and I really didn't know for sure. He didn't give me any pushback whatsoever. To the contrary, he was supportive. That conversation further strengthened a bond that was already forming between mentee and mentor.

About a week later, still prior to my surgery, we had

an advisory board meeting with those setting up the Collaborative DNA Diagnostics Laboratory. One of the folks on the board was Sam Berkman, an old friend of CEO Orrie Friedman. A living legend in the diagnostics business, Sam had cofounded BioScience Laboratories in Santa Monica many years earlier and had grown that business to become the world's largest clinical reference laboratory. BioScience eventually became known more widely under the name SmithKline Beecham Labs, which today is called Quest Diagnostics. How fortunate was I to have access to a person with such a wealth of relevant knowledge as we were embarking on this new venture?!

Sam and I had become friendly during our discussions around how to get the lab up and running, and he had introduced me to various related issues that I had never considered. This was really my first shot at operating a business, and there were so many things to learn.

During a break in the advisory board meeting, Tom and I were speaking about my upcoming surgery when Sam interjected, "I had thyroid cancer thirty years ago, at about the same age you're at now. They cut out the tumor, and I've been taking Synthroid pills every day to make up for the thyroid hormone my body doesn't make anymore. It's like taking vitamins. You don't notice it at all."

I can't tell you how extremely comforting this news was. I didn't know anyone with thyroid cancer. Sam appeared as fit and active as anyone his age. Ultimately, Sam lived a full life, passing away peacefully twenty-five years later at home in Beverly Hills at the ripe old age of ninety-five.

A few weeks later I went in for surgery. I don't recall being particularly nervous. I just wanted to get it over with, wake up on the other side, and deal with whatever new situation I found myself in. Elise, on the other hand, was at the breaking point. She was at a critical stage in her lab work and now worried that the surgeon might leave her husband with any one of a number of possible complications, such as a distorted voice for the rest of my life—or worse!

As things turned out, everything Dr. Wang had said was correct. The procedure was uneventful, the tumor was removed, and I've been taking Synthroid ever since. Few have noticed the scar, as the incision was made strategically in a natural fold in the front of my neck and stitched up tightly.

The hospital stay lasted only a few days, and I was back on the job later that week. Once my sore neck had healed, I felt the same from a physical perspective as before the surgery. Incorporating Synthroid into my routine was new, as I'd never had any reason to take a chronic medication. It took a few months of playing with doses and blood testing to get things just right.

Afterward, it was just as Sam had described. No different from taking vitamins, but with a new degree of discipline. I had to be sure I took the pills with me anytime I traveled, and I kept some on me in a pill box just in case something unexpected came up and I was away from home for a few days. There were no days off. It was a new mindset, a new responsibility, but I was confident that if I followed the program, I would live a long and healthy life.

This bout with cancer came out of nowhere and could have been extremely disruptive—especially if it had never been detected! In many respects I was lucky. First, the cancer was detected when it was still quite small, which is a tribute to the nameless general practitioner who performed my preemployment physical. Second, thyroid cancer is slow growing. Third, the prognosis after surgery is excellent, with no measurable reduction in lifespan. Fourth, by virtue of my relationship with Mike Holick, I had access to some of the best physicians in the world. And finally, thanks to my company health insurance, I had no financial burden from any of this.

Postsurgery, I came away with a new mindset. Things had changed. I had a heightened awareness of what could happen to derail one's plans, one's life. One has no control over whether or when things such as this may happen. At the same time I had a new sense of urgency, a sense of purpose, a recognition that time was finite and should not be wasted. I was determined to take advantage of my time on this planet, to be persistent in going after my goals, and to enjoy as much as I could of what life has to offer. This mindset has served me well in life and in business ever since.

GENETICS AND FORENSICS

I arrived at Collaborative with a blank sheet of paper and a broad range of new business opportunities to explore. The company's yeast technology could be used as a manufacturing platform for recombinant proteins. The genetics program was as advanced as any university research group, with projects focused on the mapping and characterization of single genes responsible for major genetic disorders, as well as the development of a range of tools to facilitate genome analysis in general. These efforts would ultimately morph into genome mapping in the days preceding the global Human Genome Project. The company was committed to creating a DNA diagnostics laboratory and still considering a variety of different genetic tests that might be offered, all based on the use of DNA probes.

Significant ethical issues surrounded the development and performance of diagnostic tests for genetic disorders, as it was unclear which actions could be taken once a disease-causing gene was detected. From a technological perspective, however, diagnosing such diseases was possible and getting easier quickly, especially for single-gene disorders such as cystic fibrosis.

It all came down to pattern matching. DNA samples would be isolated from blood and cut into fragments using molecular scissors called restriction enzymes. The resulting fragments would then be separated based on size (molecular weight) using gel electrophoresis. DNA probes that bind to known locations in the genome were allowed to hybridize with complementary targets if present in the sample. The probes were tagged with radioactive compounds. An image could then be generated by placing a sheet of photographic film next to the gel, which would be exposed in locations where radioactive probes had bound to separated fragments of DNA. The resulting image for each DNA sample resembled a series of thin horizontal bands arranged like rungs on a ladder. If a DNA sample displayed a pattern of bands previously determined to be an indicator of a certain genetic defect, then a diagnosis could be made.

The DNA markers generated through this type of analysis are referred to as restriction fragment length polymorphisms (RFLPs; pronounced "riff-flips"). RFLPs are regions of the genome that vary in length in different people and populations and are typically unrelated to any known genetic function. Their analysis enables both informative pattern matching to determine whether two individuals have the same genetic sequence (*genotype*) at a particular genomic location and more advanced genetic analysis, used for determining the location of disease-causing genes (*mapping*).

It turns out that this type of DNA pattern matching in and of itself has utility for a variety of commercial applications outside of disease gene mapping or detection. Examples include bone marrow transplantation compatibility testing, paternity testing, and forensic analysis. Over time I helped develop partnerships, raise money, write grant applications, and prepare business plans for all these opportunities. The opportunity that wound up generating the most traction the fastest, particularly from a commercial perspective, was the use of DNA probes and RFLP analysis for forensic purposes.

My focus evolved from general business development, working with each research and development team, to leading the operations of a new laboratory service business developing and delivering analytical tools. Though I didn't actually manage the lab operation, I liaised with the development program to track and help facilitate their progress and then had responsibility for further commercializing the tools they developed to drive testing business into the lab.

Key to the job was to work with external collaborators in each of the fields we pursued. The group was diverse: laboratories and organizations focused on genetic diseases;

physicians and patient advocates in the world of oncology and bone marrow transplant; and various state and federal law enforcement agencies, including the FBI. In each field I sought to establish relationships with key opinion leaders and early access customers, to build out a marketing and sales function and to license technology.

For the first time in my career, I was responsible for a business's overall financial performance. In a little over a year I had moved from exploring a broad range of exciting opportunities to being intensely focused on one in particular. I was getting my feet wet with respect to literally every aspect of operating a business.

The job got even more interesting when I was asked to be Collaborative's point of contact with the FBI Academy. My initial visit to the lab in Quantico, Virginia, was my first time back to the DC area since turning down a job offer from the Pentagon. The sprawling campus, with its green lawns and concrete-and-glass buildings, could easily have passed for an industrial park or even a university. At reception I asked for directions to Dr. Bruce Budowle's lab and was surprised that nobody first checked my background or even my ID. Or at least not with my knowledge.

Walking down the halls, I passed agents in training, all wearing standard-issue khaki slacks, sneakers, and polo shirts that seemed to be color coded in some manner. I'd pass a group wearing blue shirts, then a handful in red, and then a group of thirty or more in yellow. A few years later, in 1991, I'd see *The Silence of the Lambs* with Jodi Foster and Anthony Hopkins and excitedly tell Elise, "That's the FBI Academy! That's exactly what it looks like. And that's how people are dressed!"

Once I found Bruce's lab, I pretty much forgot I was at the FBI and switched back into grad-student mode. His lab looked and felt just like my old lab at MIT, and he acted just like any other scientist. We talked science for a bit, and I learned how far along they were in assessing various DNA typing technologies. They wanted to be able to compare two samples, such as one from a crime scene and one from a suspect, and determine whether they were from the same individual. Ultimately they aimed to create a national database of convicted criminals' DNA types to compare against crime scene samples.

I explained where we were in validating our DNA probes detecting highly informative RFLPs and the level of confidence that could be obtained in such matching experiments. Bruce was excited about testing the probes in well-understood populations of samples and jointly publishing a paper at some point. This surprised me, as I assumed the FBI wanted to keep their techniques secret.

As it turns out, it was quite to the contrary. Unless a peer-reviewed body of scientific evidence supported a new test's validity, its results could not be used in court. This was known as the Frye standard. It comes from the ruling in *Frye v. United States*, 293 F. 1013 (D.C. Cir. 1923), which states that an expert opinion is admissible only if the technique on which the opinion is based is "generally accepted" as reliable in the relevant scientific community. Bruce and I ultimately established a collaboration aimed at generating such a publication.

Competition was fierce for this business, but it was a small community and we were all on good terms. The major players in the beginning were Collaborative, Promega, and

Ray White's academic lab in Utah. We all were focused on the use of RFLPs, although we had each developed and characterized different probes. This was first-generation DNA analysis for use in identification—more specifically, analyzing probe hybridization patterns to demonstrate with great certainty that two DNA samples did *not* come from the same individual. While you could not "prove" a match, if you probed enough polymorphic loci and didn't see any differences, the likelihood that the samples came from different people became vanishingly small.

Few outside our industry were paying close attention to developments in DNA analysis. Inside the industry, however, at meetings and conferences, few could stop talking about the strides being made. I myself had participated in a landmark gathering of geneticists, forensic scientists, and other stakeholders in forensic DNA analysis held at Cold Spring Harbor's Banbury Center in 1988. I had also met with ethics think tanks, such as the Hastings Center, that were concerned about possible misuse of genetic information. I participated in a task force created by the White House Office of Technology Assessment to study the ethical issues related to DNA analysis, as well as some of the political impacts, new technological directions, and what role the government should have in funding or regulating such developments.

It wasn't until the trial of football and television star O. J. Simpson, who had been charged with murdering his wife, Nicole, and her friend Ron Goldman in 1994, that DNA analysis captured the mind of the American public. Soon DNA analysis became a mainstay of television shows, movies, and books on crime and forensic testing. All of a sudden, my little esoteric field had gone mainstream, and everyone wanted to know what we were up to.

While I was getting more absorbed in projects at Collaborative, Elise completed her MIT PhD, performed postdoctoral research in the prestigious genetics division at Harvard Medical School, and subsequently began a second postdoctoral fellowship in cancer biology back at MIT. We moved out of our basement apartment to a more spacious tenth-floor space overlooking the Boston skyline near the Longwood Medical Area. We had both come a long way but were now working as hard as ever. We had no inkling that a new technology was about to dramatically alter the world of science and our future career paths.

INTRODUCTION TO PCR

While Elise and I were devoting much of ourselves to our careers, we started consciously carving out time for other activities. We wanted to soak up as much as possible from what life had to offer, especially in the form of new experiences, places, and cultures. Often the burden fell on Elise to force me to take a break, typically when I wasn't even thinking about it, although I'm forever thankful that she did so, and did it with some frequency. She also encouraged me to push my employer, which taught me a fundamental lesson. You can't always get what you want, especially if you don't ask. If you do ask, however, to paraphrase Jagger and Richards, you may be surprised to find out that you'll get what you need.

One day, for instance, Elise told me she had booked tickets to St. Thomas in the US Virgin Islands and was leaving the next morning. I was welcome to come if I could get off work, but she was going regardless. It had just been far too long since we had taken a break. I got the message. When I arrived at the office that day, I spoke to my boss, Tom, and told him that Elise and I wanted to take a vacation. He asked when we were planning on going, and as I told him "Tomorrow," I braced myself for his response. He calmly asked how long we would be gone, and I told him a week. Tom gave me no pushback at all. He simply wished me good luck, and as I left his office I breathed a big sigh of relief.

We didn't know anything about the USVI and wound up renting a condo at Bolongo Bay on St. Thomas. The flight down was uneventful, and the humid tropical air immediately put us at ease. The complimentary rum drinks at baggage pickup didn't hurt. The condo was pretty much as advertised, on a sandy south-facing beach that was relatively quiet save for neighboring tourists. Just a few minutes away by taxi was downtown Charlotte Amalie, with its Danish-named streets from colonial times, duty-free shops, restaurants, and bars.

After a few days in the sun, we decided to take the short ferry over to St. John to see what it was like. Upon arrival we realized that we were staying on the wrong island. We fell in love with St. John at first sight. It was more lush, more laid back, less crowded, and it better fit the image we had of life on a low-key, remote Caribbean island. Two-thirds of the island was reserved as a national park, and the north-shore beaches were stunning.

We taxied in the back of a safari truck up the north-shore road to the Caneel Bay Resort, where we innocently wandered into their private Turtle Bay Clubhouse at tea-time. Sitting comfortably on the back deck, we spent the afternoon overlooking the secluded bay's gorgeous turquoise waters and sampling Caribbean beverages and appetizers. When I went to pay for our drinks, the bartender informed me that they didn't accept payment. This was a private facility open only to hotel guests and available to them at no extra charge. Nice and discreet, he escorted us out without fuss and wished us a good stay in the VI. The positive experience left an indelible mark on us.

On return to Boston, feeling rested and refreshed, I focused on building out the DNA diagnostics business beyond forensic testing. We started recruiting for a lead salesperson, as I knew nothing about how to sell such services. One candidate really stood out. Bob Giguere was just the right combination of pleasant, persistent, and persuasive, and he never stopped smiling. Everyone who interviewed him either agreed, didn't know any better, or didn't particularly care. The scientists were academics who didn't enjoy talking to salespeople anyway.

Early on I decided I needed to travel with Bob, partly to see how he performed in front of customers and partly to assist him with the pitch. Meetings with key opinion leaders were easier to get, too, if the director of the business, an MIT PhD biologist, was coming along. What I hadn't counted on was how challenging it would be to sell to biologists.

We flew coach to Ann Arbor, Michigan, and spent the

entire day walking the halls at the University of Michigan Medical School. The highlight was meeting a young Francis Collins, many years before he headed the National Institutes of Health. It was a grueling day! We must have visited fifteen labs, telling the same story over and over.

Apart from the visit with Collins, who had an ongoing collaboration with our research team, our time was spent with cold calls. The reception ranged from cool to ice cold. Most grad students and postdocs either ignored or insulted us. It was a rude awakening: I realized I had acted the same way to most sales reps when I was in graduate school. As the day wore on, I developed a deep appreciation for what a good sales rep really had to offer, and the challenges they faced in doing so. I also felt incredibly guilty and foolish for my own behavior years earlier.

I apologized to Bob once we left, but he took it all in stride and just kept smiling. "Don't give it a second's thought," he said. He knew what he was up against, and it was all just part of the job. Bob told me that regardless of what any customer's preconceptions might be, it was his job to figure out how to be of value to them. That might mean introducing them to a new technology or application, making it easier for them to order something, getting them a product for less money, or teaching them a technical trick he had learned from our own scientists. In the end it was all about building relationships and truly adding value. If you figured out how to do those two things, fewer doors would slam in your face.

Perhaps my most important unexpected event at Collaborative happened a few months later when I attended the weekly genetics R&D journal club. Senior scientist Doug

Smith was presenting a paper published in *Science* that described a new technique that enabled one to take a sample of DNA too small to work with, target specific sequences of interest, and make enough copies of them to allow analysis by conventional methods. It was analogous to pulling a needle out of a haystack and then making many copies of that needle so its characteristics could be easily analyzed.

Called the polymerase chain reaction, or PCR, this novel technique had been invented by Kary Mullis, a scientist at Cetus Corporation in Emeryville, California. A series of papers had followed from colleagues at Cetus that demonstrated various interesting applications of the technology. At the time the PCR process had to be performed manually. The DNA sample of interest had to be mixed with several reagents, followed by heating and cooling, and then this cycle repeated roughly thirty times. Before each cycle you had to add a new aliquot of DNA polymerase, the enzyme that drove the reaction.

Doug had tried to replicate Cetus's results by using his own Rube Goldberg–style apparatus. His system consisted of a metal rack containing test tubes that would be sequentially submerged into three water baths set at different temperatures. After a round of heating and cooling, the process would generate a new copy of the targeted DNA sequence for each copy present in the original DNA sample. With more cycles of heating and cooling, one copy became two, became four, became eight, became sixteen, et cetera, with an ability to keep going on as long as fresh enzyme was added for each cycle.

Doug's data showed that the process actually worked! The room was buzzing. This new process would enable applications of DNA analysis never before feasible, from all sorts of tiny samples. For many applications, DNA cloning would no longer be required. We imagined that PCR would affect many procedures that required access to, and manipulation of, DNA. It had the potential to revolutionize the field of DNA analysis—as well as many adjacent fields!

We didn't yet realize it, but Cetus and their partners at Perkin-Elmer, a large analytical instruments company, would soon form a joint venture called Perkin-Elmer Cetus Instruments and make instrument systems to automate the thermal cycling process. They would also commercialize a DNA polymerase isolated from a bacterium found in the hot springs at Yellowstone National Park, called *Thermus aquaticus* (Taq), that could withstand heating. With thermostable Taq DNA polymerase in PCR, there was no need to add fresh enzyme between each cycle, making the process much easier to automate.

The PCR technology was covered by Cetus-owned patents, and it became clear that anyone who wanted to be a major player in DNA analysis would need to have access to PCR. As director of Collaborative's DNA products and services business, my number one priority became to get a license to use PCR. My success or failure at this mission, which came completely out of the blue, would likely determine the fate of my career.

4

POLYMERASE CHAIN REACTION

UNEXPECTED JOB OFFER

I wanted to know who was responsible for licensing PCR at Cetus, and I eventually reached Dr. Ellen Daniel. They were getting a lot of inquiries, she told me, and had not yet finalized a licensing policy. Until Cetus determined how to handle licensing, we would remain in limbo. The best I could do was to stay in touch, be clear about our aims, and try to establish a friendly relationship.

Weeks turned to months, but I made sure to write or call Ellen almost weekly, and every time I went to San Francisco for other projects, I tried to stop in and visit her. One time she gave me a tour of the facility and introduced me to the PCR team, some of whom I already knew from scientific conferences. Occasionally we would go out for drinks or dinner. The business relationship didn't seem to progress, but we established that we enjoyed interacting with each other.

Meanwhile I continued working with the Collaborative genetics group on grant applications to finance development of tests for single-gene disorders. Eric Lander, a mathematician interested in genetics, had recently joined MIT's Whitehead Institute and Collaborative's scientific advisory board. He became actively engaged in Collaborative's attempt to showcase a first-generation map of the entire human genome. That project culminated with publication in the journal *Cell* of the first map spanning the entire human genome with three hundred genetic markers, which were all RFLPs. A major scientific achievement, truly, which would have gotten more press attention if the stock market hadn't crashed that same week, in October 1987.

The published map did get the attention of big pharmaceutical companies, however, all of whom were now interested in working with us to localize, identify, and characterize disease-causing genes. Yet whereas Collaborative had shown what was possible, it had not yet developed a dense enough map with enough markers to have the value that Orrie insisted upon. As a result, deals didn't get done, and parties too often went their separate ways. I became frustrated, as did everyone else working on these projects. At some point key people started leaving the company.

One day, without warning, Ellen Daniel from Cetus called. She still had no significant update on licensing, but she wanted to discuss another matter. Perkin-Elmer Cetus was seeking someone to manage the PCR research reagents business full time. It was an unusual situation because the person would be a Perkin-Elmer employee but would live in

California and work full time at Cetus. The staff who reported to them would be Cetus employees, so the new hire had to be someone the Cetus folks would feel good about working for, someone with strong leadership qualities who could command their respect.

Might I be interested?

"Absolutely," I replied.

I could hear the smile in her voice, and I could feel the smile on my face. This could be the high-impact opportunity I'd been seeking. What's more, Elise's frustration with MIT's internal lab politics and ethics was growing, and she would probably be thrilled to get out of that hornet's nest and move to the genetics group at Cetus. I just needed to convince the people at Perkin-Elmer that I was the right person for the job. I had met a few of them at forensic-testing conferences, so I wasn't a completely unknown entity.

Soon I spoke with a half dozen people at Perkin-Elmer, and all the calls seemed to go well. That was followed by weeks of silence. I called Ellen to see if there were any concerns. None that she knew of, she told me, but she offered to find out what was holding things up. A few days later my phone rang, and a man with a slight Italian accent began speaking.

"Hello, Stan. This is Riccardo Pigliucci from Perkin-Elmer. I'm calling regarding the job opening that you've interviewed for."

"Hello, Riccardo. Thanks so much for calling."

"Stan, let me get right to the point, as I know you've been patiently waiting for some feedback from us for weeks now, and I have to apologize for that. Stan, first let me tell you that from everything I've heard, uniformly, everyone who has spoken with you has enjoyed their conversation and feels you are eminently qualified for this job."

I breathed a sigh of relief.

"The problem on our end," he went on, "is that the person who was leading the job search is no longer with the company. We've been scrambling to figure out how to reorganize in light of his departure and for the time being have decided that I'm going to take on his former role overseeing Perkin-Elmer's biopharma business. That means that the person we hire to manage the PCR reagents business will report to me."

"I see," I said, not understanding the implications.

"So here's the situation. All of the feedback on you has been great so far. This is a very important hire for us, however, and I can't responsibly offer this position to someone I've never spoken with and never met. I'm wondering if we might find a time to meet for lunch or dinner to talk about this in person?"

"Absolutely," I replied. "What are you doing tonight? I can leave here by 2:00 p.m. and easily be in Norwalk for a 6:00 p.m. dinner, if that works for you."

"Really?! That would be great! There's a place nearby in Westport called the Mansion Clam House. I'll have my secretary book reservations for us, and plan on seeing you there at six."

"Sounds good. I look forward to it!"

"Me too."

I wasn't particularly nervous about this interview, but a bit antsy. I hadn't given much thought to what we might discuss, and just wanted to get this dinner over with. I reached the restaurant and sat at the table for fifteen minutes before a distinguished-looking man in a gray suit and combed-back black hair appeared at the front door. After the man exchanged a few words with the maître d', I knew he was Riccardo. They both headed in my direction, and I stood to greet him. We shook hands, said hello, and took our seats.

After a few pleasantries Riccardo suggested we order a bottle of wine. "Have you ever had the Stags' Leap chardonnay?" he asked.

"It sounds familiar, but I'm honestly not a white wine expert. I'm happy to try anything you think might be good."

"It's usually fairly dry but smooth. Let's give it a try."

A few minutes later the waiter brought us a bottle, showed Riccardo the label, uncorked it, and poured a small amount for each of us. I gave it the requisite sniff before taking a sip, swirling it around my mouth, and swallowing. Riccardo did much the same, tilting his head down in thought.

He looked up at me. "What do you think?"

"To be perfectly honest," I said, "it's more bitter than other chardonnays I've had. I'm not sure if it's this bottle or the wine, but I'm not really thrilled with it."

I was being honest. I don't think I had ever turned back a bottle of wine, especially when someone else was buying. And especially at an interview dinner. The proper thing would probably have been to just say "It's great" and move on, but for some reason that's not what I did.

Riccardo leaned forward as if to share a secret. "You know what? I was thinking exactly the same thing!" He turned to the waiter. "Let's send this one back, and please bring us a bottle of your 1986 Simi chardonnay."

It's funny how ordinary interactions such as these can

reveal so much about a person—their tastes, their honesty, whether they are intimidated by people or situations, and their sense of the relative importance of appearance and process as compared with getting what they want. This moment was a real icebreaker. We received our Simi chardonnay, toasted to our meeting, and placed our dinner orders.

As we sipped the wine, we exchanged stories about our backgrounds, and over the next two hours the conversation morphed into a discussion of the opportunity at hand. At some point Riccardo asked, "Stan, have you ever fired anyone?"

I was completely unprepared for this question, and puzzled by it. I had little interviewing experience and hadn't read up on standard questions or practiced anything. I was just being me. I wasn't sure what kind of answer he sought, but I had the distinct impression that a yes would be the better answer. Unfortunately that wouldn't be truthful.

"Riccardo, you know, I haven't had the opportunity to manage many people before. I know you'd probably prefer someone with more managerial experience, but it's just a matter of fact. I had one person working for me when I was consulting, and most of the team at Collaborative were peers. My secretary and sales director were really my only two direct reports, and I wasn't dissatisfied with either of them. I don't believe I'd have a problem firing someone if the situation called for it, but to this point it just hasn't been an issue."

A look of concern came over his face. "Well, this is something you're likely to encounter if you come to work with us. There will be many more people working for you, and you have to consider the impact of a poor performer on the health of the business, as well as on the morale of the rest of the team. Someone who is either incapable, lazy, or has bad judgment won't just fail in their own role but also create risks for the entire business, and therefore for the jobs of everyone else who is working hard to accomplish their goals. So you have to be prepared to get rid of people who are not performing at an acceptable level or who may be a bad influence for whatever reason."

Point taken. Hopefully this lack of experience wouldn't cost me the job.

Between sips of coffees and bites of homemade cheese-cake, Riccardo continued. "Stan, I have to be honest with you. This is a very important hire for us. Everyone speaks highly of you, and I've very much enjoyed our conversation. Normally this would be the type of job I'd want to give to someone I've known twenty years, not twenty minutes. Do you understand what's at stake here?"

"Yes, I understand, and I hope to have a chance to prove to you that your trust in me and my capabilities is war-ranted. I very much want this job, and I'll do everything I can to make this business successful for all of us. There's a lot riding on it for me too." This was my close. Asking for the order.

I thought he might say something such as "Well, let's think it over" or "Let me talk with a few others," but I would come to learn that Riccardo felt strongly about making de-cisions quickly, moving forward, and then dealing with the consequences. In fact, I've never met anyone else in my ca-reer who was as comfortable making decisions. He wasn't reckless, mind you. He was a smart man who knew what he knew and understood the risks but felt that there was an advantage to making decisions quickly and moving forward.

"Okay," he responded. "Let's make it happen."

⋈⋈⋈

WELCOME TO CALIFORNIA

If you've been in business long enough or had responsibility for a large enough operation, you've probably seen clauses in contracts referring to acts of God such as tornadoes, volcanic eruptions, or earthquakes. When developing their first or second business plan, most aspiring entrepreneurs are not seriously thinking about such random and relatively infrequent events. If any one of these should happen, it usually occurs with little to no warning.

Elise and I took an early flight from Boston to SFO the morning of October 17, 1989. We planned to stay two weeks and find a house to rent for a year. Low-rise apartment complexes in the Emeryville "flats" offered short-term leases and were close to Cetus. By the end of the day we settled on an apartment in a relatively new wood-frame building three stories tall.

Around 5:00 p.m. we found ourselves sitting around a conference table in the apartment management office on the top floor, ready to fill out a lease. I was vaguely aware that the World Series was getting underway across the bay, with the San Francisco Giants hosting the Oakland Athletics.

That was a big deal locally, but being a native New Yorker and having lived in Boston for ten years, I frankly wasn't paying much attention if the Yankees or Red Sox weren't playing.

I started filling out the lease, and when I got about halfway down the page, I felt the table vibrating. With a sense of awe and excitement, I turned to Elise and said, "Wow, I think we're having an earthquake."

Suddenly it felt as if someone had cranked up the volume on the speakers to ten. The room shook hard. The wall before me became a flexible membrane bowing in and out. Windows burst and sprayed glass everywhere as bookcases came tumbling down. From Elise's vantage point she could see streetlamps swaying back and forth as if constructed of rubber. The real estate agent sat back in her chair and started screaming, "My God, it's the Big One!"

I don't know how much time had elapsed, but my excitement quickly turned to terror as I realized that the whole building could collapse. I tried to remember what to do in an earthquake. Someone was already standing in the doorjamb. Should I jump up and try to squeeze in too? There was no time to think. I needed to act. I tried to dive beneath the table, but the best I could do was wedge myself into the space between my chair and the table in front of me. And then the shaking stopped.

I scrambled back up into my chair, and we all exchanged glances, nobody quite sure what to say or do. Turning to Elise, I said somewhat uncomfortably, "Maybe we should come back and deal with this tomorrow."

She looked back at me, completely unfazed. "Let's just

do it now. It's like I told you. They have earthquakes in California."

"Obviously," I replied, "but I don't think they often have earthquakes like this."

The real estate agent concurred. She babbled about how this must have been the Big One, and we survived, and we experienced it together so we would forever be bonded by this shared experience. Welcome to California! I quickly completed the lease, securing an apartment for the next two weeks, and we headed out the door.

The street below was eerily quiet. It was a gorgeous afternoon, seventy degrees, no humidity, with a brilliant blue sky and almost no wind. The traffic lights were out, and none of the cars were moving. Power was out everywhere. We'd later learn that the elevated freeway had collapsed in Emeryville and Oakland, as did a portion of the upper span of the Bay Bridge. A massive fire was raging in San Francisco's Marina District, and plumes of smoke could be seen rising from the Oakland Hills.

Elise was scheduled to give a seminar to the human genetics group at Cetus the next day, but we doubted that would go on as planned. We spent the early evening in our car in the hotel parking lot listening to news reports on the radio and sharing stories with other stunned travelers. Nobody was being allowed back into the building. After four hours or so we were finally able to get back into the hotel and, after a few drinks at the bar, calm down enough to fall asleep.

The next morning we discovered the quake had been centered near Santa Cruz, a coastal college town to the south between San Jose and Monterey. It hit on the San Andreas Fault and measured 6.9 on the Richter scale. They called it the Loma Prieta earthquake. It was the biggest quake to hit the Bay Area since 1906, and there was extensive damage in a number of isolated spots. Our meetings at Cetus had been postponed. Having nothing better to do, we decided this would be the perfect time to go look at rental homes. It would be obvious which ones could withstand a major earthquake!

That day we visited a number of depressingly expensive or unacceptable spots. Within a week, however, we struck gold. We found a cute little house on Burton Drive, at the very top of the Oakland Hills in Montclair, a block higher even than Skyline Boulevard. It was small but built into the hillside and had a deck off the main floor with a built-in hot tub. On some days you could sit in the hot tub and look down on the clouds below, seeing the tops of the pine trees sticking through, and perhaps the orange tips of the Golden Gate Bridge in the distance. It was a great location and fit our budget.

A few days later, as things were slowly getting back to normal and most of the major streets were cleared for traffic, Elise gave her seminar at Cetus. It was well received, as we expected. We both started our new jobs a week or so later. Our commute was just fifteen minutes, down the Oakland Hills to the flats of Emeryville. I made a mental note to never stop when driving underneath an overpass.

Perkin-Elmer Cetus was essentially a start-up grown within a billion-dollar diversified analytical instruments business. A joint venture between a large multinational corporation, Perkin-Elmer, and a small biotech company, Cetus, it was managed in a very unconventional manner. All Perkin-Elmer Cetus employees were actually full-time employees of either Perkin-Elmer or Cetus, and most had jobs unrelated to the joint venture and committed only part of their time to Perkin-Elmer Cetus. The entity was overseen by a management committee that acted much like a board, comprising executives representing both companies. I was one of the first employees hired with a full-time focus on the joint venture. A Perkin-Elmer employee, but based at Cetus, I was responsible for a business segment operated entirely by Cetus employees.

I needed to have strong interpersonal and persuasion skills, because nobody on my team actually reported to me (at least in the beginning). Many of my skills in this respect were no doubt influenced by my interactions with family and friends and by my experience as a teenager trying to keep the peace between fighting parents. It helped, too, to have grown up in diverse Greenburgh, New York, spent summers forging friendships at Camp Abelard, and just been a teenager in New York City in the early 1970s. My experience forming relationships in college and thereafter didn't hurt either. Many of my fundamental values and approaches to dealing with people had been consistent since an early age.

My primary responsibility at Perkin-Elmer Cetus was to oversee product strategy, product development, marketing communications, and sales. Cetus handled reagent research, development, and manufacturing—over which I had no control, though I was still held accountable (e.g., if we ever had any kind of backlog or quality issue). Our leading product was Taq DNA polymerase, the enzyme that drove DNA replication and was the crux of the PCR process. When I arrived we were just beginning to launch recombinant Taq DNA polymerase sold under the brand name AmpliTaq DNA Polymerase (or AmpliTaq for short).

DNA thermal cycler instruments that automated the PCR process were developed in Norwalk, Connecticut, with research, development, and marketing managed by a separate business unit under the leadership of Donna Marie Seyfried. Both Donna Marie and I reported to the Perkin-Elmer Cetus management committee, and more directly to Riccardo Pigliucci, then president of Perkin-Elmer's instruments group. We were expected to coordinate our efforts, and we shared many support resources. We also interacted with many academic and industrial laboratories around the globe. Donna Marie was instrumental in introducing me to many aspects of how business worked at Perkin-Elmer.

In the beginning, the international aspect of Perkin-Elmer's business was a complete mystery to me. At some point, however, it dawned on me that each country organization had its own annual financial targets and was not required to sell any particular product to hit those targets. They weren't selling just PCR products but rather the entire Perkin-Elmer portfolio. As a consequence, the salespeople sold only the products they best understood and were confident their customers would buy. This meant that my teammates and I had to go out on the road and help each country office recruit and train people who could sell our products. I had to coordinate a team effort to teach representatives of each country's business organization the benefits and key selling points of our products, introduce them to key opinion leaders, help establish collaborations they could leverage, and in general convince them that they could exceed their overall country sales targets by focusing more of their resources on selling PCR products.

None of us had any idea just how big the PCR business would become. A survey conducted by the marketing group a year or two earlier, when nobody had yet heard of this technology, revealed (predictably) that scientists had no idea what they'd use it for so wouldn't likely purchase. Marketing projected one hundred units sold worldwide in the first year. I heard a rumor that Riccardo couldn't justify having a business segment that generated less than a million dollars a year, so he decided that the thermal cycler would be priced at $10,000 apiece.

Our price point turned out to be high compared to those of eventual competitors, but the market was much larger than projected, and we had the benefit of being first to market and more. We had a widely recognized brand name and a reputation for high quality, backed by a strong service and support organization and an overwhelming patent position.

My first meeting with the management committee came just weeks after the Loma Prieta earthquake. Riccardo was flying into SFO overnight from Bangkok, so we agreed to meet at the Ernst & Young building in San Francisco. I had to take the ferry from Oakland because a collapsed span of the Bay Bridge was still being repaired.

The boat ride was fun. Rather than fight traffic, I basked in the sun and enjoyed the bay's cool morning breeze as I sat and sipped coffee. I wasn't as pleased when I reached our meeting room on the fortieth floor of a steel-and-glass skyscraper. I wondered the whole time what I would do if the ground started shaking again. We all settled in and got down to business, a mundane agenda until we discussed who'd be responsible for selling products into the forensic analysis market—a long-contentious matter only vaguely covered in the original joint venture agreement.

Bill Gerber, head of Cetus's PCR division, and Bill Sawch, general counsel at Perkin-Elmer, hotly debated who should have control and why, and at some point began throwing verbal barbs at each other across the table. Out of the corner of my eye, I noticed Riccardo slowly packing and snapping shut his briefcase. He then stood up, picked up his things, and headed for the door. The room fell silent.

He stopped and turned around. "I just flew all night long to be at this meeting and got almost no sleep. Now I have to listen to you whine like little children and throw insults at each other. I've had enough. I won't do this anymore. If we can't trust each other and figure out how to work together as true partners, then let's dissolve the joint venture right now."

What a power display. I stopped thinking about earthquakes and wondered if I was still going to have a job at the end of the day.

Thankfully the two Bills apologized, and everyone settled down. It was quickly agreed that Cetus should manage the forensics business and we should stop debating the point. I was relieved I still had a job. Trust between partners is something I came to embrace that day more than ever before, and many times since I have been reminded of just how critical it is to the success of any business.

✕✕✕

HITTING OUR STRIDE

Plenty of calls and trips to Connecticut helped me realize that Dr. J. Fenton Williams and Anne Sawyer could be strong allies and people I'd enjoy interacting with in the PCR group in Norwalk. Fenton was a PhD fluorescence spectroscopist by training who became one of the world's leading authorities on PCR. He would go on to build the first and best global applications support network and knowledge base for PCR and was a fountain of knowledge and good cheer. Anne was responsible for marketing communications. Both would go on to build teams with whom I interacted regularly, and they all did their best to make me feel part of the PCR family despite the distance between us. Within a few months we would find ourselves on the phone daily and shooting faxes back and forth across country just as frequently.

We tried to create an enjoyable workplace before such notions came into vogue in Silicon Valley, starting slowly and in small ways but gaining steam over the next few years. We typically started our days with espressos and lattes from local coffee shops (before Starbucks was a thing). Daily we'd create "meme faxes" by cutting pictures or text from newspapers or magazines, pasting them onto fresh pieces of paper, copying them, and faxing them between the PCR groups in Emeryville and Norwalk. Each of us tried to outdo the other and help take the edge off. Everyone participated, but Fenton was the master meme faxer. I can only imagine what fun he would have had if social media had existed back then.

We often grabbed lunch together, either at a local restaurant or from the taco trucks that lined up outside of

Cetus. When visiting Norwalk I'd recruit groups for basket-ball games at the seldom-used court in the parking lot. In California it was either basketball or tennis. Most of us were young and healthy, and rarely was it hard to find enough people for some kind of athletic event. We once even played laser tag, back when it was still a novelty.

If we weren't participating ourselves, we went on out-ings to baseball or football games. Sometimes our signifi-cant others would join us for barbecues and picnics. One day I volunteered to bring dessert to lunch and was mocked mercilessly for bringing a watermelon (some apparently do not consider this fruit a worthy "dessert"). I never intended to bring an inadequate dessert, but I was pleased that my employees were comfortable making fun of me to my face.

Anytime the team assembled—from either coast or with our sales representatives—it was cause for a group dinner. These dinners always involved music, sometimes dancing, and often singing. This was especially true when we were meeting in Europe or Asia. For example, over dinner at a sales meeting in Salzburg, Austria, we wrote and sang about Taq DNA polymerase to the tune of "Smoke Gets in Your Eyes."

> They, asked me if I knew,
> About P-F-U,
> I of course replied,
> It won't amp-li-fy,
> Taq's what you should try
>
> They, asked me how it went
> When I tried out Vent

I of course replied
It won't amp-li-fy,
Taq's what you should buy

The song went on for many verses, each one mocking competitive enzymes such as Pfu, Vent, and others. Once it was time to leave the restaurant, we wandered through the Christkindlmarkt sampling sausages while drinking warm glühwein (a mix of red wine, orange, rum, and cinnamon) and enjoying the Christmas spirit.

These events were typical for us, and word about the culture we were creating in the PCR business spread throughout the company. Every country sales group across Perkin-Elmer looked forward to our visits. In between visits, we made sure to stay as connected as possible with our fellow PCR mates through faxes, phone calls, and a monthly newsletter with contributions from associates around the globe.

Our Taq DNA polymerase business was now growing exponentially, and people throughout Perkin-Elmer took notice. One day I received a message that Riccardo was visiting Emeryville and wanted me to give him a tour of our manufacturing operation. By then I had been become familiar with the facility, but I was a bit embarrassed—there wasn't much to show. Our entire production operation fit in one small room. A few tabletop fermenters dotted one lab bench, the chromatography system for enzyme purification another. The room couldn't have taken up more than two hundred square feet.

The entrance was up a flight of grated steel stairs that looked like a fire escape (it might have been one!). I escorted

Riccardo up and explained what the items in the room were in a minute or two, then meekly apologized for having little to show him. But he just broke out into a big smile, put his arm around my shoulder, and said, "This, my friend, is a beautiful thing."

We were selling Taq at a price of $0.62 per unit, in vials that contained 250 units, with 1.25 units required per standard 50 µL PCR. Since the specific activity of Taq is 292,000 units per milligram, a full gram of this protein would sell at a list price of $181 million and could be used to conduct 234 million PCRs. At our list price we were generating gross margins in the range of 98 percent, with the most expensive part of the product being the plastic tube that carried the enzyme. If you google "the most expensive substance on earth by weight," the answer that comes up is "The radioactive element Californium, first made in 1950, is the most valuable at $27 million per gram." Taq is almost seven times as valuable and costs very little to manufacture.

Riccardo was right. This, indeed, is a beautiful thing. He provided an important insight I hadn't appreciated about gross margins, low cost of goods sold, and scalable manufacturing infrastructure. There is a powerful strategic advantage to having a simple, low-cost manufacturing process that requires very little capital to scale.

Another insight I gleaned from Riccardo was the importance of tightly managing expenses around the end of each quarter, and in particular the last six weeks of the year. Perkin-Elmer was a publicly traded company, and market analysts closely watched the company's quarterly profitability versus expectations. Unexpected events can dramatically affect the value of a publicly traded company's stock.

Performance above expectations typically drives prices higher, and coming in below expectations pushes prices lower. When the end of the year approached, Riccardo—in an effort to control expenses—would not approve three things: new hires, travel, or advertising. We all planned accordingly.

In early 1990 the growth of our business was accelerating, but competition was emerging. Companies were flooding scientific journals with advertisements for Taq DNA polymerase and temperature cycling machines, never mentioning any particular application such as PCR but dramatically undercutting us on price. Our senior team was getting increasingly frustrated by the emergence of low-priced competition and the frequency and boldness of their advertisements.

It was bad enough we had a strong patent position and weren't suing competitors, many felt, but we also weren't running ads ourselves. We were looking like a big company that had taken the business for granted or was too foolish to realize its value. We were hearing about it from our sales reps, as their key customers were bugging them.

A meeting of the management committee had been planned to convene in San Jose at the offices of Perkin-Elmer Nelson. Gaynor Kelley, the chairman of Perkin-Elmer, would fly out for the gathering. Perkin-Elmer Nelson was a relatively new entity formed through Perkin-Elmer's recent acquisition of Nelson Analytical. Their core business involved the development, manufacturing, and sales of data integrators for use with chromatography systems and other laboratory information management systems.

Founder Dave Nelson had been asked to join the

Perkin-Elmer Cetus management committee, given his knowledge of the life science markets. Another key player from Nelson Analytical, Dr. Robert "Bob" Board, had taken over Riccardo's temporary role leading the PCR business. By the time of the meeting I had already been reporting to Bob for several months.

Bob was a good-natured fellow, around 5'10", with a full head of hair and accompanying bushy mustache. Imagine a blond Sam Elliott. He typically dressed in old worn blue jeans or chinos and a flannel shirt and spoke with a western rancher's twang (think "Howdy, partner"). We hit it off immediately. He lived in the hills above Redwood City, great for working in San Jose but an excessive commute to Emeryville.

Bob drove a little old dark British Racing Green MGB roadster. He tended to show up around 10:00 a.m. and leave around 3:30 or 4:00 p.m. I rarely saw anything in his office except an empty desk and notes scribbled on a whiteboard or handwritten in a notebook he carried around. He seemed carefree, but he was intensely competitive and driven. That sort of mix suited me well.

Bob had an amazing talent for looking at complex situations and rapidly homing in on the most critical issues. One day I told him how much I admired this skill and asked how he had developed it. He insisted it was because he was fundamentally lazy. That surprised me, but he explained that being lazy was a huge advantage: he quickly figured out what really mattered and ignored the rest.

As with many of my mentors, Bob had incredible soft skills. Most enjoyed working with him, although his independence and insistence on doing things a certain way frustrated some. Or perhaps they were just jealous. I usually found Bob easygoing, but he could be hard as nails when he made up his mind or when it came to delivering on promises. He insisted that meetings start on time, so latecomers might find the door locked. Or be fined a quarter once let in the door. He also prevented anyone from monopolizing the discussion. Everyone had a chance to speak.

Another characteristic Bob shared with many of my mentors was his understanding of the importance of creating a fun environment, where everyone bought into a shared vision, felt like part of a team on a mission, and enjoyed their jobs. He combined an appreciation for one's personal life (family, hobbies, sports, travel, music, arts) with absolute determination when it came to work. He was tolerant by nature, and he always stood by his word. I don't mean to paint a picture of a saint, but Bob was a man of strong convictions and great integrity, and he fostered loyalty in all those who worked with him. A true leader.

Shortly after Bob's arrival I had recruited Valerie Erdman to lead our marketing efforts. She was coming from a job in reagent marketing and sales at Pharmacia in Canada, a major international player in our space. Val turned out to be a great collaborator and contributor and easily my most important hire at that point. We shared a common vision and a strong drive to achieve our goals, and we worked well together in both developing new strategies and executing on plans. Val was eager to launch a much more comprehensive marketing program, starting with more aggressive advertising.

Valerie, Fenton, and I gathered together advertisements from competitors for our management committee meeting in San Jose, showing the fierce price competition we faced. Bob gave the presentation, literally flipping through one ad after another using transparencies and an old-fashioned overhead projector.

At some point Gaynor had seen enough. He slammed his fist on the table and stood. "Who the hell told you not to advertise?!" he growled.

The room fell silent, and Riccardo seemed to slowly slump down in his chair. It was the first, and possibly only, time I had seen him so intimidated.

Riccardo finally confessed. Pausing advertising was just a short-term interruption with the goal of maximizing quarterly profits, he explained.

Gaynor would have none of it. He glared at Riccardo for a moment and surveyed the room. "Let me tell you all something. A technology with the growth potential of PCR comes around maybe once in a generation. If you're ever so fortunate to have access to something like this, you need to constantly be advertising, constantly driving home your message of leadership in the field."

Based on Gaynor's comments, the very next day Bob began a search for an advertising agency to work with the PCR business. We wound up choosing Lena Chow Advertising, which was the start of a relationship between Lena and me that continues to this day. Lena is a real pro. Having come out of the pharmaceutical industry, she made her mark with high-quality graphics, strong messaging, and a clean style that resonated with people like me. Lena taught me not only about advertising but also about product positioning, promotion, image, brand, and style. This was an absolutely critical relationship, and it might never have happened if we hadn't been limiting our advertising spending to maximize quarterly profits.

⤬⤬⤬

FIRST TRIP TO JAPAN

I had long been fascinated with Japan, in part because my father had served there in World War II, and also because we hosted a Japanese foreign student in our home for a few months when I was ten or eleven years old. My mom had been actively involved with the Experiment in International Living, a Vermont-based group that placed international students with American families for a month or two at a time. The stories I had heard left me with vivid images of Japanese temples and Mount Fuji, and I couldn't wait for the opportunity to see them for myself. None of these stories, however, adequately prepared me for my first trip there.

In June 1990 Fenton and I traveled to Perkin-Elmer's Japanese office in Yokohama to meet with the company's Asia-Pacific sales representatives and provide a day of training on PCR technology and sales. Attendees came from Korea, Thailand, Malaysia, Singapore, Australia, Taiwan, and China, not to mention Japan. Perkin-Elmer Japan had decided not to sell PCR products directly but rather to partner with a company that had a better understanding of the Japanese molecular biology research market. So all the Japanese trainees actually worked for Takara Shuzo, a Kyoto-based company whose primary business was making and selling sake and other alcoholic beverages. In fact, at the time Takara had a plant in Berkeley and was the largest producer of sake in the United States. They also had a small and growing research biochemicals business.

We flew from Newark to Narita, the airport that serves Tokyo, and the flight was long enough that corporate policy allowed us to fly business class. This was a big deal, as most of our travel entailed paying as little as possible. We flew on a 747 jumbo jet and were thrilled to be on the second floor in oversize seats with extra legroom. We spent sixteen hours in the air, by far the longest flight I had ever taken. Fenton brought battery-powered candles and red checkerboard linens for our table setups, which ensured extra-special attention from the flight attendants. We dined on Japanese bento boxes served shortly after takeoff, drank far too much sake, slept for nearly six hours, and woke up with another eight hours to go.

Jet lag left us in altered states of mind upon arrival. We were unprepared for the bright-red-uniformed hostesses who greeted us with smiles and bows at the airport subway station and ensured we made it onto the correct train. We weren't quite sure who was supposed to bow lower, and the awkward moment was followed by hysterical laughter once the train doors closed. Two hours later we arrived at Yokohama Station, which resembles New York's Grand Central, both architecturally and in terms of crowd size and the variety of restaurants, stores, signage, and colored lights in every direction. I loved the energy of the place and was ready to explore this beehive of activity.

Though nothing was written in English, we somehow made our way to street level. Bright lights, flashing neon signs, and honking horns surrounded us, and we had no sense of direction. Following an old paper map, we eventually found some landmarks and navigated the four-block journey to the Cosmo Hotel. On virtually every street corner, vendors cooked traditional snacks from lantern-draped carts that gave off a sweet, smoky, enticing aroma.

The Cosmo's rooms were typical for a Japanese business hotel, just large enough to fit a single bed from which you could reach out and touch both walls. The electric toilet with all sorts of buttons and lights was far too complicated to figure out between fatigue and mental confusion, but fortunately a simple push-button flush did the trick. After a short, restless night, it was time to brew some instant coffee, shower, dress, and cross the street to the office.

The pace of the meeting was slow. Most spoke English except some of the Japanese, so we had an interpreter repeating every sentence we said, just after we said it. The interpreter turned out to be Dr. Kiyozo Asada, Takara's most senior research scientist, likely chosen for the interpretation gig due to his command of English and his keen interest in our technology.

I would put a slide up, speak a line or two, stop, and then Asada-san would translate. Fenton and I never knew whether the translations were accurate. It was a long day, and we struggled to stay awake given the jet lag. For the longest time, no one asked questions, and we started to suspect that doing so was considered culturally embarrassing or perhaps even insulting.

Come midafternoon one of the attendees finally spoke up and was quite animated. Asada-san responded in kind, and then the two of them went back and forth for several minutes in heated discussion. Fenton and I exchanged quizzical glances, and finally the gentleman who had asked the question stopped, and Asada-san turned to us to speak. "Reply canceled," he said. Apparently whatever issue had been raised had been resolved. It was a very strange session.

A very long session too. In the early 1990s it was typical for Japanese to work long hours. They might commute by train up to two hours each way, arrive at the office by 7:00 a.m., and stay late. Fenton and I kept going, fueled by adrenaline and caffeine, until around 7:00 p.m. when Asada-san informed us that we were finished for the day. Secretaries rolled in a table filled with various Takara beverages. Before the trip I had been given some quick lessons on Japanese business etiquette, so I made sure to pick up a bottle of expensive Johnnie Walker Black Label whisky at the Newark airport to present to the local office manager. I was just waiting for the right time.

People started congregating and popping open beverages, and Fenton and I were intrigued and amused by some of the names of these drinks. One, "Green Banana Fizz," was particularly humorous given our altered state of mind. The can's graphics sported a purple banana on a green background, the significance of which Fenton and I inferred. We started drinking. Clear, green, and bubbly, it tasted something like sparkling apple-banana juice but carried a real punch. After a few glasses everyone started mingling and talking in broken English.

We met people from a half dozen countries, and many asked questions nobody brought up during the formal session. Nick Samaras, an Australian sales manager roughly our age, spoke English as his native tongue and shared tales of traveling all over Southeast Asia helping to establish our

PCR business. Nick would become our most trusted ally and closest friend in this part of the world, often providing valuable advice on local customs and contacts.

Someone picked up the microphone we had used for our lecture and started singing. Karaoke time had begun. When a Korean woman finished her song, Fenton and I grabbed the microphone and started in on Liza Minelli's "New York, New York."

Suddenly a door opened, and in came an older Japanese gentleman of medium build in a white shirt and black tie, with slicked-back black hair. The look on his face was both severe and ominous, although we couldn't be sure if he was angry or just puzzled. We soon figured out that this was the Japanese site manager, Izumi-san, and we were singing in his office. He grabbed the microphone from Fenton, and for a moment I worried we had broken protocol and were about to be thrown out for disrespecting his office. To our surprise and relief, Izumi-san picked up where we had left off and started singing in perfect English! Realizing all was good, the rest of us chimed in for the final verse in unison, ending with a long, drawn-out "New York, New York!" followed by smiles, cheers, and toasts all around.

Afterward I returned to my chair, reached into my backpack, and pulled out the Johnnie Walker Black. As I walked toward Izumi-san, a lower-level office manager swooped in to receive the gift and pass it off to a staff assistant to whisk it away. Protocol had been breached, however innocently. Was it improper to hand a gift to the site manager directly? Or was Johnnie Walker Black not of sufficient quality? Or not properly wrapped? We never found out. So much to learn, like never laying down one's chopsticks crossed. Only parallel!

Izumi-san recognized my gesture with a polite nod, a small bow, and a big smile. I knew all would be fine from then on—which turned out to be a long night that didn't end until the wee hours of the morning, after we had visited several private clubs and somehow dined along the way. I doubt any of us slept more than two hours that night, which made the following day of training even more challenging. Our relationship, however, had been cemented. Now we were all friends and working together, and they were committed not to disappoint us.

BOB'S BUSINESS PLAN

Strategic planning is critical to any start-up operation. There are a series of basic questions I typically consider when determining whether to participate in new business opportunities or invest in early-stage companies: "What's the product? Who's the customer? Why do they care?" Following close behind are "Is it real? Can we win? So what?"

While at Perkin-Elmer I learned to ask these questions, the answers to which began to form the basis for a plan. The planning process continues for the life of the company, and the document one uses to capture all the information is truly a "living document." It's meant to be modified in real time as new information comes to light. At different times in the company's life, some version of this plan may be used to guide your operations and support fundraising, partnering, recruiting, and investor relations.

In the early 1990s it wasn't unusual to develop a detailed fifty-to-sixty-page document covering every aspect of the business. I can't think of anyone with the patience to wade through all that information anymore. Nowadays a ten-to-twenty-slide PowerPoint is more commonplace, along with a one-to-two-page executive summary.

The first time I was involved in developing a shorter, more focused presentation was in late 1990, toward the end of my first year as PCR reagents business unit manager. We had three big issues at the time. The first was how to leverage our intellectual property (IP) position, which was strong but still being attacked as the market opportunity became apparent to those who wanted a piece of the PCR business. The second was our need to focus, as we had far more ideas for products to develop than we could possibly support given our annual operating budget. The third was how to solidify our relationships with key customers and ensure they viewed us as the premier and preferred supplier in the marketplace.

As autumn rolled around, we knew we needed to develop an annual business plan, required of all Perkin-Elmer's businesses every year. The task was to develop a winning strategy in the marketplace and a plan of action and to write that up in a detailed and lengthy document. A typical Perkin-Elmer business would have essentially their entire management team working for a few months to develop an enormous document that would be sent up to corporate for review. Once completed, it would sit on a shelf somewhere gathering dust.

Our business was growing rapidly that year, and we never had enough people to keep up, despite the fact that everyone worked long hours every day—largely because the work was incredibly exciting and we had a great sense of shared vision and mission. In that kind of environment, it was hard to imagine how any of us could drop what we were doing for a month or two and prepare a conventional business plan. On the other hand, we knew we were playing in a dynamic space and had to have a well-thought-out strategy to drive our business forward.

To my great surprise, our general manager Bob Board unilaterally decided that we would take a different approach, and somehow he managed to get upper management at Perkin-Elmer to buy in. We would meet for a single day, in person in a conference room in Norwalk, and hammer out our strategy and action plan in one long whiteboard session. Then we would document that on one sheet of paper, front and back. This new approach forced us to focus our energy intensely, work together as a team, and develop something concise and useful in a time- and cost-effective manner. This experience changed my view on the nature and utility of the process forever.

Our strategy ultimately hinged on a few key points. The first was leveraging our strong IP position while assuming that we couldn't rely on patents for more than a few years. Next were two selling points others couldn't name without violating patents: promoting our premium-priced products as being higher quality and backed by an explicit "PCR performance guarantee," and establishing strong customer relationships through a PCR applications support function unsurpassed in quality worldwide. And finally, based on the close relationships we would develop with key opinion leaders, gaining access to market intelligence about important emerging applications and then focusing our finite research and development resources on addressing those applications that customers demanded the most.

Though we had issued patents covering our instrumentation, key reagents, and the PCR process itself, we decided to act as if those patents simply gave us a two-year lead time over major competitors. It's not that we didn't believe in the strength of the patents, but we had to build a moat to prevent intruders who challenged or simply ignored them. We also needed to prepare for a day when it might make sense to issue licenses to these patents.

In the case of both thermal cyclers and Taq DNA polymerase, the popularity of PCR became so strong that our customers knew others were selling similar products. Competitors simply ran advertisements that talked about instruments that heated and cooled samples and DNA polymerases, with no explicit reference to PCR but showing thermal cycling graphics. When we complained to our lawyers, they informed us about the principle of substantial noninfringing use. If one could argue that a product had another use beyond the patented process, and it was substantial, we couldn't prevent them from selling their products. Of course, their customers would be infringing our patents by using the nonlicensed products in a patented process, PCR, but nobody ever wins in the marketplace by suing their customers.

Our solution was to make PCR quality an issue of concern for customers, and support for PCR a hallmark of our business and a differentiator from the competition. We had

Lena Chow develop a logo for a "PCR performance guarantee," and we sold a set of lambda DNA control reagents that were guaranteed to work in PCR with our other standard PCR reagents and our PCR protocols. This enabled scientists to confirm that their reagents were working as advertised, provided they were purchased from us and used on our instrument systems. Competitors could not offer anything similar.

We created the world's most comprehensive PCR support network, led by Fenton. He pulled together a staff of scientists available in all time zones by phone or fax and accessible from anywhere. They published application notes regularly, as well as a monthly user newsletter titled "Amplifications." They held PCR seminars and conferences and hosted workshops to teach PCR in laboratories at the Norwalk office. They collaborated with key opinion leading scientists and published papers together. We supported various educational organizations with donations of products and sponsorships of programs. All under the banner of "Perkin-Elmer Cetus" and the "PCR performance guarantee."

At the end of the day this campaign cemented our brand image as the highest quality and highest value. Our product performance and support efforts contributed to our strategy of delighting customers, helping them advance their research, and becoming trusted friends and colleagues. We employed leading PCR scientists in our laboratories, collaborated closely with influencers in academia and industry, and provided them, too, with the highest-quality products and support. Everyone wanted to work with us. We sold our products at prices significantly higher than competitors.

However, when you purchased from Perkin-Elmer Cetus, you got not only a great product, but also access to a club that included the world's top scientists.

Ultimately it was these relationships that would last long term, provide access to reliable and current market intelligence, enable us to deliver new products our customers needed, and allow us to weather competitive threats. It was critical that we focus our research, development, and marketing activities, as we had finite human and financial resources and endless opportunities. Our deep understanding of our customers' needs and desires helped us make these choices. For each new product we chose to pursue, we came up with high-level timelines and milestones.

This entire effort required dedication, creativity, operational efficiency, and a willingness to break some rules. We had to move fast, share a common vision and mission, and commit to working as a team and finding a way to have fun in the process so we wouldn't get burned out. In a self-fulfilling way, by being successful we had fun, and that fun provided the motivation to experience it again.

Over the next three years annual sales of PCR products grew from less than $10 million in 1989 to over $100 million while generating 30 percent net profits. Just five years earlier most customers didn't even know what PCR was, and nobody could have anticipated its impact. Our initial marketing projections suggested we might sell one hundred systems per year, but we wound up selling over twenty thousand in less than five years. This experience made me forever skeptical about any projections regarding what the world would look like five years into the future.

✕✕✕

KARY IN NEW ORLEANS

According to my mom, the first word I ever said was *more*. I'm pretty sure I was a talkative child. My grandfather on my mother's side, Al "AJ" Herman, used to kiddingly chide me, saying, "God gave you two ears, two eyes, and one mouth. Use them accordingly."

I was reminded of this in June 1990 when I had the pleasure of first meeting Kary Mullis, who invented the polymerase chain reaction. Kary would go on to receive the Nobel Prize in Chemistry in 1993 for this invention. I'd highly recommend reading the story of his conception of PCR in his book *Dancing Naked in the Mind Field* or his 1990 *Scientific American* article "The Unusual Origin of the Polymerase Chain Reaction."

First published in *Science* in late 1985 and patented by June 1987, PCR took the world of molecular biology by storm. Taq DNA polymerase was named molecule of the year by *Science* in December 1989. Kary was a rock star in our field. Anne Sawyer, who was responsible for Perkin-Elmer Cetus marketing at the time, had arranged for Kary to talk at a major annual scientific conference we sponsored in New Orleans. The day of the event, the one-thousand-seat auditorium was jammed, with folks standing in back and sitting in the aisles. Not only was Kary famous for his invention, but he was also infamous for his presentation style and some of his unconventional thoughts.

A typical Kary Mullis presentation included graphs. Most scientists would display such material on a white or blue background, but Kary got more creative. He showed his data overlying fractal images in the background. Each slide looked like a psychedelic light show from the 1960s. He often included a slide of the earth revolving around the sun, as a reminder to be open minded. That was all good fun, but when he started using nude female models in his slides, many in the audience were taken aback.

He'd get to the point in his presentation where he discussed the automation of PCR and put up a slide showing the original DNA thermal cycler. "Here was the original model," Kary said as the audience saw a picture of a nondescript analytical instrument with a naked woman draped over it. An uncomfortable mix of gasps and giggles followed. Kary would continue, unfazed. "That model wasn't ideal, so we came up with a new one." The next slide showed a different box and a different naked woman in an even more suggestive pose. Now a few in the audience would actually boo. This became extremely uncomfortable for those of us sponsoring his talks.

Kary was also notorious for disbelieving that HIV caused AIDS, despite this being widely accepted in the scientific community. A small band of contrarians, led by Peter Duesberg at Berkeley, were looking for alternative hypotheses, and Kary was one of them. At a Cold Spring Harbor conference four years later, where we celebrated a "Decade of PCR," James Watson (director of Cold Spring Harbor Laboratory, co-discoverer of the structure of DNA, and Nobel Prize winner) pulled Kary aside beforehand and pleaded with him not to talk about HIV that night. Of course, when Kary got up to speak, he immediately told everyone about his discussion with Jim and then, with a smirk, promised to say no more—he had already said his piece.

Back on that evening in June 1990, Anne Sawyer had arranged a big dinner celebration for Perkin-Elmer Cetus people at the conference, with Kary as the guest of honor. Around 7:00 p.m. we had all filtered into the Jackson Brewery, in a private top-floor room that overlooked the Mississippi River on one side and down into the French Quarter on the other. By 8:00 p.m. Kary had not arrived, so we ordered appetizers and drinks. By 9:00 p.m. Kary was still a no-show, so we ordered dinner.

Around 10:30 p.m., as we were perusing the dessert menu, in walks Kary. "Hey, everybody, am I too late for dinner?"

What could you say? "Hey, Kary, we're about to order dessert, but grab a menu and feel free to order whatever you like"? The guest of honor sat himself in the middle of a long table surrounded by more than a dozen people, and we started to introduce ourselves. Kary was wearing a Hawaiian shirt, a straw hat, shorts, and flip-flops and already appeared inebriated. When Anne introduced herself, the games began.

"Oh, you're Anne Sawyer!" Kary blurted out. "Your name is on my hotel reservation. You guys think of everything. So glad we're spending the night together." Anne was an attractive woman, around 5' 6", slender, with shoulder-length blond hair, and she had a professional air to her. Clothes from Talbots. She also had a healthy sense of humor and a well-developed skill for quick comebacks from harassing men.

"No, Kary, that's *your* room. I just made the reservation."

"Oh, Anne, I'm sorry if I gave away our secret. I didn't mean to embarrass you. But now that it's out there, let's just not worry about it."

"Kary, you can do whatever you want in *your* room to-night, but I won't be involved." Anne was still smiling, being friendly and polite yet firm—but probably getting annoyed.

It just kept going from there. People valiantly stepped in, trying to help deflect Kary's attention from Anne, but every five or ten minutes he'd come back with another push at her. Thankfully his dinner arrived, and after a few bites he seemed to sober up, or maybe his attention had just shifted.

Suddenly he launched into a new monologue. "Have I told you all about the movie script I'm writing?" he asked. "It's a story of space travel hundreds of years in the future."

Over the next hour or so Kary went on to describe the plot in detail, its climax involving an intergalactic beer transport shuttle hit by a meteor shower and spraying tril-lions of beer droplets throughout the universe. Most of us couldn't keep track but tried to humor him.

The clock now past midnight, people politely excused themselves so they could get a few hours of sleep before meet-ing with customers or staffing the exhibit booth the next day.

Undeterred, Kary stood. "Anyone want to join me in the French Quarter for a few drinks?"

I could see that most of my colleagues were not thrilled. Newly in charge, feeling some sense of responsibility to our guest, and thinking this could be an interesting opportu-nity, I spoke up. "Yes, I'll go." A moment later Christian Oste joined in: "Me too." Christian, among many other things, held the distinction of having introduced more people to

PCR than anyone I know. For years he traveled the world lecturing in halls as full as the one we had seen that day, evangelizing on behalf of PCR. I was about to paint the town with two rock stars, and I was looking forward to the adventure, come what may.

The next few hours were a blur. We wandered the Quarter in the wee hours, stopping in Bourbon Street's bars, strip joints, and jazz clubs. We were just roaming around, drinking and chatting and taking in the sights New Orleans is famous for.

Shortly after 3:00 a.m. we found ourselves sitting curbside, drunk and desperate for a break from the music, the lights, and the crowds. At least I was sitting. Kary still stood, so I was looking up at him in a darkness lit only by a streetlight, a haze in the air and in my head. Christian asked Kary something innocuous, "So what else have you been up to recently?" perhaps.

Never one to miss an opening, Kary jumped right in. "Did you see that paper about amplifying ancient DNA from fossils? The possibility of reconstructing dinosaur genomes? Well, I started thinking it would be pretty cool to amplify dinosaur DNA, package it in crystalline lockets, and sell them at the Nature Store. They have stores popping up all over the place."

"Great idea," I chimed in, "but I have a better one. Why don't we go to Graceland and get some of Elvis's DNA from hair in an old comb or in a toothbrush. We could amplify that and sell it in lockets next to the *National Inquirer* at every grocery store checkout in the country!"

Kary's eyes almost popped out of his head. "That's a *great* idea! Why didn't I think of that?!"

"In fact," I went on, "why stop at Elvis? We could amplify John Lennon's DNA and sell that to every Beatles fan in the world!"

Christian piled on. "This is totally scalable! You could amplify DNA from celebrities of all types, of all generations, as long as you could get some of their hair."

Kary was bobbing back and forth now, almost dancing in place with joy, and we all started laughing uncontrollably. Then, in all seriousness, he said, "You guys need to quit your jobs today. Forget about Perkin-Elmer. Come back to La Jolla with me and we'll start a new company. We can do this!"

It was far too late, and I was far too drunk, to make serious decisions. "I don't know . . ."

"Yes, do it!" Kary implored. "Quit your jobs!"

My head was spinning, and I finally conceded that the night was over. "Kary, it's been fun, but I gotta go. I need to get up again in less than three hours to be at the booth by eight."

With that we called it a night, and each wandered off in separate directions, me—and I'm pretty sure Christian—returning to our hotels and Kary probably heading out for another round.

Four years later during a meeting at Applied Biosystems, someone asked if I happened to know Kary. "Sure, we've met a few times," I said. "Let me tell you about the first time." Then I regaled him with the New Orleans story.

"Well, Kary is one of our advisors, and I speak with him every few weeks," he said. "I'll say hi for you."

A week later the gentleman called me back. "I honestly didn't believe that story you told me about Kary in New

Orleans," he said, excited, "as so many people try to take credit for his ideas. But when I mentioned that we met and started to recount it, Kary immediately remembered and confirmed it was your idea. You probably don't know this, but he actually *did* start a company that amplifies and sells celebrity DNA. It's called Stargene, and they have funding from one of the major baseball card companies, I believe Topps. He said if you want a position on the board in honor of your idea, he'd be happy to propose it."

I was floored. I had never been a board member and had no idea what Perkin-Elmer's policy was about that. I thanked him and told him to thank Kary and wish him all the best. "I'll check with my superiors to see if I could do that," I said. I never followed up on that one.

That night in 1990 I took advantage of an unexpected opportunity and wound up building a long-term relationship with a key figure in our field, generating incalculable goodwill, taking part in a fun story for us all to share, and proposing an actual new business idea. Over the years I've met many who think Kary a nut, a crazy man who got lucky one night when he had a novel idea. I believe Kary just thinks differently. His mind isn't wired the same. I don't believe he's a genius, and I don't condone some of his behavior or his outlandish, damaging views, as with HIV/AIDS. However, the real lesson of Kary Mullis, at least for me, is that new ideas can come at any time, from any person. Keep your eyes and ears open and listen to everyone. As Grandpa Al said, "Use them accordingly."

5

NEW APPROACHES TO DNA ANALYSIS

VACATION IN CLEVELAND

"What we know about the future is poor; things that look bad can be the greatest luck and vice versa; sometimes you have to take a chance." My paternal grandfather, Paul Rose, said that in 1948, ten years after leaving Nazi Germany to start a new life in America. My dad kept the original quote handwritten in pencil on an index card in a box of memorabilia I found after his death. I have no living memory of Paul, who passed away when I was two weeks old, but over the years those words have meant a lot to me.

I arrived at one such decision point in my life in the fall of 1991. Recently I had been confidentially informed that Cetus was going to be acquired by the end of the year. The ramifications for Perkin-Elmer Cetus were unclear, which meant that the continued existence of my job was questionable. I tried my best to keep abreast of the acquisition's progress and in the meantime polished up my résumé and discreetly inquired into other opportunities.

One day my former mentor Tom Oesterling called to update me on progress at the new company he had founded when he left Collaborative Research. It was a biopharma start-up developing drugs for neurological disorders. The company was based in Cleveland, Ohio, which wasn't a selling point for me, but they were building out a team for a planned initial public offering (IPO). Tom asked if I would be interested in joining him as VP of business development, with a healthy pre-IPO stock grant that could become very valuable. Given that my current job might be disappearing, the opportunity intrigued me.

Soon thereafter I learned that Cetus would be sold to Chiron and that Roche was going to acquire the rights to PCR. There was tremendous uncertainty about what the future would look like at Perkin-Elmer after the dissolution of the joint venture. Perhaps Roche would enter some kind of partnership with Perkin-Elmer to address the research market, but maybe not. After all, Roche had their own research products business, Roche Applied Science. In this scenario Perkin-Elmer would have to get something for their partial ownership of the joint venture, but that could just be a cash payment.

Tom said he and his new business had a lot of support from the local community and that the genetics department at Case Western would love to welcome Elise. Biotech millionaires were being minted weekly, so Elise and I began seriously considering this opportunity. Tom planned to take the company public within six months, which left plenty of time for her to sort things out with Case Western.

We ultimately decided that the position in Tom's company was just too attractive to pass up, and I gave Perkin-Elmer notice at year's end. The deals with Chiron and Roche were announced shortly thereafter. As it turned out, Perkin-Elmer partnered with Roche and retained rights to make, market, and sell PCR products into the research and applied markets (excluding diagnostics). Elise didn't want to move from California, especially in the dead of winter, so we agreed that I'd head east in advance to help prepare for the IPO. I wound up renting a basement apartment in Cleveland, enduring the dark, cold, snowy winter, and working around the clock.

From a purely careerist perspective, this turned out to be a really interesting time. I essentially took a crash immersion course in IPO preparation. We worked on the S-1 registration statement the old-fashioned way, in mahogany-and walnut-paneled law offices with catered meals, hot towels in the bathroom, and manservants to care for our every need. With a dozen lawyers and as many bankers and company leaders sitting around a large conference table, we hammered through draft after draft of the S-1. Since I was living alone and had no local social life, I never really had to go home. I worked around the clock—and it was fun! We all had visions of a big payday.

By the time April 1992 rolled around, however, the market had taken a turn for the worse. For the first time I heard the words "The window has closed." Inexperienced with these things and having paid attention to the stock market only over the past few years, I never considered that certain eras just weren't ideal for a public offering. Yet this is exactly what we were facing, and we had to pull the plug on the IPO.

Adding insult to injury, when Elise joined me in the spring, she was treated outright rudely at Case Western. In their view I had a high-profile job in town so my wife had no choice but to join me, regardless of what they offered her. What's more, we had just bought a home in Cleveland Heights, so she was really stuck. Essentially handcuffed, she was given the smallest possible salary and title, despite having just received a generous NIH grant that would cover her lab plus overhead for the next three years. It was pure sexism, and neither of us would stand for it.

I was no longer having fun at the new job either. I was never particularly passionate about the company's products. Sure, I had long been fascinated with neurobiology, and I enjoyed working with Tom and trusted him, but I didn't feel comfortable with the rest of the staff. What's more, now that the IPO had been abandoned, my day job had become boring. I was tasked with finding corporate strategic partnerships for a company that had only preclinical data on its lead drug candidate, was based in Cleveland, and was running low on money. That's not an attractive combination.

By summer we were psychologically done and needed to find an exit. Out of the blue, Peter Barrett called me. He was leading Perkin-Elmer's life sciences division, and under the new strategic partnership with Roche, the PCR business reported to him.

"Hey, Stan. So, tell me, do you hate Cleveland yet?" he asked. He wanted me back at Perkin-Elmer, and his timing couldn't be more perfect.

✕✕✕

LAND OF THE TALL BLUE FLOWERS

It's been said you can never go home again, and in many respects this notion applied to our California homecoming. We were thrilled to leave the Rust Belt and return to gold rush country, but we couldn't possibly have anticipated some of the events that would follow. After only a week of stressful house hunting, with rental prices having soared during our absence, we struck gold. Thanks to Elise's persistence in pushing me to look at houses that appeared far too expensive for us to rent, we stumbled into an incredible house-sitting opportunity.

In exchange for watching a dog for two years while the owner studied in Paris, we got to live in a spectacular ranch home on Skyline Boulevard along the crest of the Oakland Hills. The property was enormous—two-and-a-half acres—and included an in-ground pool and a barbecue pit large enough to roast a pig. Along the house's entire western side was a gigantic deck offering sunset views of San Francisco, spanning from the Oakland Bay Bridge, past the Golden Gate, and as far north as the Richmond–San Rafael Bridge. I referred to it as the "hotel deck."

Elise had been offered, and accepted, a job working on new approaches to automated DNA sequencing at Applied Biosystems (ABI). She had to drive forty-five minutes south to Foster City, but she enjoyed the ride across the eight-mile-long San Mateo Bridge. I would be driving south, too, but not nearly as far. The PCR business now resided in a modern office park in Alameda, an island just off Oakland in the San Francisco Bay. Roche had their offices in the building directly next to us.

Walking into the new office in Alameda, one couldn't help but notice the tall blue flowers lining the sidewalk— *Agapanthus africanus* (*A. orientalis*), a.k.a. blue lily of the Nile. It was a classic California cookie-cutter one-story office park occupied by early-stage businesses and established companies that needed extra space or a local geographical outpost. Everything was clean and new, a big change from the converted old brick factory building where Perkin-Elmer Cetus was located just a few miles north in Emeryville.

I was relieved to be back in my old job but keenly aware that in my absence the business had been through a relocation and a period of continued growth. Valerie Erdman, whom I had hired a few years earlier as marketing manager and who had grown to become my most trusted partner, had stepped up in my absence. She was reporting to Peter Barrett under the new organization that had emerged from the dissolution of the joint venture and the creation of the new strategic partnership between Perkin-Elmer and Roche.

I'm not sure what I expected, but simply dropping back into the same role was not in the cards. There were new people, new relationships, and new issues to contend with. On the other hand, much of the business had not fundamentally changed. A few former Cetus employees had joined our team, and we were searching for a few new people. Settled was the old debate over the forensic analysis market, as it was now an application area served by Perkin-Elmer. Valerie began reporting to me again, our relationship as comfortable and productive as ever. By necessity, and because she had earned it, Val took on much more responsibility going forward. This gave me time to recalibrate, to focus on the fresh issues confronting the business, and to travel the world presenting the new business goals for PCR to the rest of the Perkin-Elmer organization.

Soon the Perkin-Elmer team in Alameda grew, with Val recruiting and hiring most of the new product managers and supporting staff. Roche hired a new point person in the relationship with Perkin-Elmer. Otherwise most of the people we interacted with at Roche were former partners from Cetus. It all felt very familiar—until it didn't. That's to say that the new people had a noticeable influence, as did the emerging corporate culture at what was now Roche.

A new degree of separateness and secrecy had developed between the two companies, and the condescension from some of our Roche colleagues bordered on arrogance. Perhaps the new leadership at the entity now called Roche Molecular Systems had encouraged this division. We had always been partners employed by two different companies, but suddenly some no longer treated us as members of the same team.

It didn't help that we were now physically separated except when we gathered for weekly product development meetings. Gone were the informal hallway discussions and the mingling common during the Perkin-Elmer Cetus days. Moreover, some at Roche felt that research and development was their sole responsibility and seemed thrilled that they no longer had to consider input from marketing and sales people at Perkin-Elmer. This created some real challenges for the business whenever issues needed input from both sides.

Those of us on the Perkin-Elmer side tried not to let this new attitude get to us, as we were all busy and having a pretty good time. Our new team members were uniformly dedicated, upbeat, and well suited for their roles. I honestly never thought about it until someone mentioned it, but aside from me the entire group was female, and included people of European, Asian, Latino, and African American descent. We were the most diverse business unit within Perkin-Elmer and well ahead of our time. Most importantly, we developed a great working environment, proved to be a very effective team, and had good fun in the process.

Occasionally in the afternoon the team would lock the front door, turn up the music, and dance in the hall for ten minutes or so. I'm not sure whose idea that was (not mine!), but it was perfectly in line with the culture we had tried to create and helped everyone blow off some steam and feel good about their job. Often we'd start the morning by bringing in cappuccinos and lattes from a local coffee shop, and at lunch we'd walk over to Nellie's Tacos as a group and grab a carnitas taco or two.

One of our major initiatives was a communications program we were working on with Lena Chow to reassure customers that the Perkin-Elmer Cetus products they had come to rely on would continue to be available and made the same way, with the same high quality, from Perkin-Elmer. We modified the PCR performance guarantee so that it now came from Perkin-Elmer instead of Perkin-Elmer Cetus, and prepared a series of direct mailing campaigns and print-ad placements in journals. The plan worked well, based on extensive follow-up surveys and continued sales growth. We had successfully transitioned our customer base.

We also had to ensure that our global sales affiliates within Perkin-Elmer understood our new messaging and had supporting graphics and text from us that could be translated into local languages. This meant I spent a lot of time visiting sales offices across the US and worldwide. Usually accompanied by Fenton or Valerie and/or someone on the local sales or support team, I would give seminars at universities and meet with the PCR applications specialists to brief them on our newest products and applications. We were keeping the business focused given the size of the opportunity, but our portfolio was expanding, and so was our sales volume.

As I traveled Europe visiting offices, I learned of a new phenomenon affecting our business. Prices for our products varied wildly from one country to the next. Our products were manufactured in the US (reagents in California, instruments in Puerto Rico) and imported to a central warehouse in the Netherlands. Customer transactions were structured so that profits were taken by Perkin-Elmer in Zug, Switzerland. The system was designed to maximize favorable tax treatment.

Individual country sales offices could charge in-country end users whatever price they wanted. Local competition still affected pricing decisions, but if customers in a given country wanted to buy our products, then they had little choice but to pay whatever the Perkin-Elmer sales office charged. Realizing they could maximize their overall financial performance based on sales of PCR products, some of the sales offices got greedy. Since the scientific community is connected on a global basis, and people talk, this started to create an uncomfortable situation for our brand, which was viewed as taking advantage of customers in certain countries.

We tried hard to convince the country sales offices that

this short-term windfall would hurt them in the long run. Some listened, some didn't. A few years later, an event that we (at least I) didn't see coming changed all that. Once the European Union (EU) was formed in November 1993, customers in one EU country could purchase from a supplier in another EU country. This created some conflict within Perkin-Elmer Europe, as the Italian sales manager, for example, did not want the German sales manager to accept orders from a customer based in Italy. It was virtually impossible—and illegal—to stop. Within about a year, all the country sales offices wound up selling at the same end user prices for fear of losing their customers.

Back in the USA, another longtime activity would also lead to an unexpected event. Two years earlier I had completed my first business-to-business deal at Perkin-Elmer Cetus by selling large quantities of AmpliTaq DNA Polymerase to ABI for use in their DNA sequencing kits. Unbeknownst to me, the companies had for years discussed the possibility of merging. One day in 1993 I learned those discussions had heated up again, and this time it appeared as if both parties were seriously interested. I was asked to join a small team on the Perkin-Elmer side to plan and negotiate the merger.

My hands were full, but I realized this would be a big deal. PCR had already transformed the world of molecular biology research and applications, and ABI was far and away the leading supplier of automated systems for DNA synthesis and DNA sequencing. Combining these companies would create a market leader in genome analysis tools addressing a rapidly growing field. My own role after such a merger was unclear, but I wasn't too concerned. I naively assumed that since Perkin-Elmer was the larger company, it would be in control, and my role would likely be significant as the PCR business would remain key.

Despite being a core member of the Perkin-Elmer negotiating team, I was still in a background role and not sitting at the table with ABI. As with any deal, it's not over till it's over. Given how focused we all were on growing our own businesses, we had to take with a grain of salt the notion that we would ever get to a close.

When the deal was finally done, celebratory phone calls and emails abounded. As the immediate euphoria passed, however, we had a lot of unanswered questions. Most of all, everyone wanted to know, "What does this mean for me?"

$$\bowtie\!\!\bowtie$$

PE APPLIED BIOSYSTEMS

Beyond a well-scripted press release, at first management had few answers regarding how the newly merged company would operate together or how it would affect specific employees. Awkwardness ensued, and everyone realized that some internal messaging and communication was urgent. Many had their own ideas about how the operation should run and what their roles should be, so the rumor mill was in full swing.

To quell the confusion, management informed us that an integration process would soon begin. It would take several months, during which we would figure out how to work with one another and settle on everyone's role. Meantime, the party line was to express excitement for the deal, enthusiastically support our partner's products, technologies, and people, and begin working with a team of consultants to determine how to best organize and operate as a combined entity. As unexpected as the merger itself was, even more unexpected was the operating structure that would emerge.

The biggest impact, aside from some personnel changes, was that the PCR business would merge into the old ABI business. The fact that ABI would run PCR, even though Perkin-Elmer had acquired *them*, not only was unexpected but also received poorly by Perkin-Elmer's rank and file. We had built this business, after all, and we thought we still best understood the technology, the markets, the applications, the customers, and product development and manufacturing. Certain people at ABI had different ideas regarding how things should be run and which opportunities should be prioritized, and we vigorously debated our disagreements.

I was now heading up the new PCR business unit, including both reagents and instruments combined. Our research and development efforts, however, were operating under separate leadership in a matrixed organizational structure. More significantly, I was in the uneasy position of having to please a new master, one everyone suspected wanted to replace me with someone they knew and trusted. I was reminded of what Riccardo Pigliucci said when he'd first hired me to manage the PCR reagents business. This was a job he "would prefer to give to someone he'd known for twenty years, not twenty minutes." My new superiors at ABI surely thought the same. I wouldn't be their top choice no matter how well I had performed.

The PCR business had become the newly merged

company's crown jewel. As noted in the *San Francisco Chronicle* on October 13, 1993, "PCR is so ubiquitous today that researchers now refer to it as the 'Swiss Army knife' of molecular biology." With so much on the line, the pressure to keep outperforming was high, and I didn't want to provide any rationale to replace me. I had to muster support for the new organizational structure, which could be difficult if I disagreed with their management decisions. I had to stand up for what I felt was right for the business and for the people who had worked so hard to create value in it.

Despite all these concerns, there were many bright sides to this new relationship. One of the great benefits of working at ABI was being introduced to a variety of business approaches and processes I hadn't been exposed to previously. Perkin-Elmer had deep expertise in all functional areas of business and had developed processes long proved effective. ABI was more open to new ideas and had adopted some relatively novel approaches to their business operations, many of which originated in Silicon Valley. I wound up utilizing these for many years thereafter, and they were invaluable when it came time to launch my own independent businesses.

I learned about Geoffrey Moore's *Crossing the Chasm* and its approach to the strategic planning, marketing, and sales of technology-based products. The approach begins with identifying a meaningful problem that you want to solve and a solution you believe is compelling. Focusing on key opinion leading (KOL) early adopters in a market segment of great strategic value is critical to success, with the objective of rapidly developing a commanding position in that niche.

You consider your desired competitive positioning based on compelling features of the solution you're providing and a sense of how best to message that to customers. You assemble the whole-product solution (including accessories, services, partners, and allies), offering everything your customers need to be successful (fulfilling their "compelling reason to buy"), and rapidly get KOL customers to purchase, be thrilled with their experience, and generate good word-of-mouth buzz in the marketplace. Once a leading market position is taken, you grow by leveraging your success to move from early thought leaders to mainstream customers (across the chasm) and then into adjacent market niches with new KOLs.

The use of phase-gated product development programs and launch plans was another valuable approach learned at ABI. All projects move from concept to research and past a "start development checkpoint" where a thorough review and approval are required before transitioning from research to development. There was another gate to pass through to get approval to start commercial activities, and a third gate to formally launch the product. Even postlaunch, there was yet another checkpoint at which you assessed whether every aspect of commercialization was going well.

All department directors were trained on how to handle oneself in public-facing interviews. The process involved developing a one-page interview guide I found extremely helpful for presenting to all sorts of audiences. This involved splitting a single sheet of paper into four quadrants and listing

- the five most important points you wanted to get across;

- the five most challenging questions you could imagine being asked (and your answers);
- three to five experts you could refer the interviewer to for more information; and
- key facts regarding your product (numbers and data).

At ABI I had my first exposure to quarterly business reviews, in which each business segment presented to senior management across all business segments its high-level strategy, goals for the coming quarter and year, and brief overviews of major programs underway or planned—and solicited constructive feedback on the plans. There was also a rolling forecast of sales by quarter, looking ahead two years, which was updated every three months.

Last but not least, ABI had a useful approach to personal goal setting and annual performance reviews for all employees. Aside from evaluations based on contributions to the corporate and business unit goals, each employee had their own four to six goals for the year that were designed to be unambiguous, measurable, challenging, and achievable. Having everyone properly focused, with goals aligned and expectations set, helped reduce surprises—which would happen nonetheless.

From an operating perspective, we had several significant product launches during this period. All contributed to the PCR business unit's unprecedented growth. On the reagents side, these included new enzymes offering improved performance for specific applications, as well as accessory products that could be used to make the PCR process more uniform or easier to perform. There was also a host of specific application-oriented kits launched in fields including infectious disease research, gene expression analysis, forensic testing, environmental testing, agriculture, and veterinary science.

On the instrument-systems side, under the direction of Murray Anderson, we launched the new GeneAmp PCR 2400. It was designed for personal use by an individual scientist, analogous to recently introduced personal computers, and had an intuitive user interface. Nicknamed the "personal DNA thermal cycler," the 2400 was a huge success. Our group also began work on the first novel analytical system developed as a collaboration between the old Perkin-Elmer engineering group in Norwalk, our new merged team in Foster City, and our partners at Roche in Alameda. Named the PE-ABI 7700 Real Time DNA Thermal Cycler, this system automated a process called *real-time PCR*, which enabled quantitative measurements of amplified DNA. The 7700 would go on to open up an entirely new market for quantitative PCR analysis that was especially useful in diagnostic applications.

Despite all this good news, a significant problem was brewing. The Human Genome Project was gearing up, with designated Human Genome Project centers funded by the National Institutes of Health as well as the US Department of Energy. Other large core laboratories serving major research centers were also scaling up their activities. This growth required dramatic increases in PCRs being run, yet our sales representatives notified us that they were beginning to see reductions in use of Taq DNA polymerase. As it turned out, the enzyme's price had become such a strain on program budgets that these big laboratories were resorting to obtaining clones of the *Thermus aquaticus* bacterium, growing them in tabletop incubators, and extracting their own home-brewed polymerase enzyme. Just as the big players do with the home brew distillers in backwoods Appalachia, we had a bootlegging problem.

Top management wanted to go to university licensing offices and demand they respect our patents and threaten to sue if they didn't cease bootlegging or pay us a fair royalty. I strongly opposed this approach, as you never want to sue your key customers. Not only does it further piss them off, but they wind up influencing the entire market.

At the annual Cold Spring Harbor genome sequencing meeting that fall, I met with Eric Lander, who was vocal in the scientific community and headed the country's largest genome center at MIT's Whitehead Institute. At the time we were selling Taq for sixty-two cents a unit. Eric and I took a walk in the woods one afternoon and discussed the problem. Our high prices were impeding scientific progress, he said, and furthermore, this project was a national strategic priority. Our discussion was amicable but not comfortable.

I got right to the point: "So how low do we need to go?"

We both stopped walking as he thought for a moment. "We need the price to be a penny a unit."

My jaw dropped. "There's no way we can get to that price," I blurted out before backpedaling a bit and adding, "but let me go back and talk with my colleagues and see if we can do something meaningful."

On the way back to California I had a hard time thinking about anything else. This was going to be a disaster if we couldn't come up with a reasonable response. I knew we couldn't possibly get to one cent, but what could we do? And then it came to me! We'd have to be willing to take a big hit with these largest customers to protect our position with the rest of the market, which was growing rapidly. The biggest cost components in Taq are the packaging and the labor to dispense small volumes into tiny tubes. What if we agreed to sell large quantities of Taq DNA polymerase, but only if provided in single large vials, say 250,000 units instead of 250 units? This would be offered only to US-government-designated Human Genome centers. That would give us some cover to drop the per-unit price substantially for this one segment of the market without affecting the price at which we sold Taq to the broader research community and destroying our business.

But that's not all. To effectively provide an even greater discount, and to generate goodwill in the community, what if we also offered to provide in-kind grants in the form of free Taq? We could match the same quantities as purchased, but again only in bulk and only to genome centers. Everyone agreed this could do the trick. This program dropped the price from sixty-two cents to twenty-four cents a unit for bulk Taq, and then with the matching gift and a large enough annual commitment the price went down to ten cents a unit. This was still an order of magnitude higher than what Eric was seeking, but would it be enough to shut down the bootleggers?

We presented the proposal to Eric as well as to Francis Collins, head of the Human Genome Project. I had known them since my days at Collaborative Research, when Eric was a math wizard just beginning to learn about genetics and Francis was an associate professor at Michigan who was unknown outside of genetic research circles. They trusted me when I told them this was the best I could do, and that continuing to violate our patents would ultimately be bad for their institutions, the US government, and the field of science. They agreed.

As we left the room, I went up to Eric to thank him for his support. "Thanks for understanding, Eric. We tried to really think outside of the box here, but there was no way to get down to a penny a unit."

With a big smile he said, "I know. I never expected you to get down to a penny. But this is a huge step from where you were, and if I had asked for ten cents you probably would never have gotten below a quarter."

Eric was absolutely right. Within days we had a joint press release with the backing of all the Human Genome center directors. Within months most bootlegging ended, including 100 percent of the activity at the genome centers. Our business continued to grow at the prior pace, given that genome mapping was always an outlier market segment, and the goodwill we generated further distinguished our business as the global leader in PCR. Listening to customers, flexibility and open-mindedness, leveraging relationships, knowing our BATNA (best alternative to a negotiated agreement)—all contributed to overcoming a major and unexpected challenge.

Life in Foster City was now much more laid back than during the early days in Emeryville or Alameda. We'd routinely take long lunches or leave early to catch happy hour at a local bar. Almost every day we'd take breaks to play basketball, tennis, or soccer. Elise and I were now living in Half Moon Bay, where every weekend seemed to bring blue skies and gorgeous beach weather despite its reputation for being foggy and cold.

I joined a men's basketball league that played night games at the local high school. Basketball had been a passion of mine ever since growing up in Greenburgh, and I tried to find places to play everywhere I lived. As a young boy I played for hours every day, rain or shine, often until it got too dark to see the rim—or until I could hear my mom calling for me to come home for dinner. I'm not talking about sanctioned games now, but pickup games, out in the street, anywhere I could find a hoop.

If you showed up at a court and a game was going on, you'd have to call "Next" and wait for the first two teams to finish before your chance to play. Once your team took the court, you could only continue to play so long as you won. Competition was brutal, even as a ten-year-old. If you couldn't play well enough to contribute to a team win, then you wouldn't be picked to play with whoever called "Next," and you might never get to play again that day. Even worse, you might get a reputation as a loser and be ostracized by the other kids. Fear of failure can be a powerful motivator. The fear of missing out on fun can be too.

Basketball reinforced the lessons my parents had taught me about judging people based on their skills and the way they treated others and nothing else. It didn't matter what they looked like, how they dressed, how they spoke, or where they came from. Were they skilled? Were they team players? Were they people you could trust with "Next" on the line? Just as importantly, through my love of basketball I found a vehicle to meet new people and develop new relationships, many of which would never otherwise have formed.

Basketball kept my body healthy and my head clear. Life was relatively easy now. We lived by the beach and had a short commute to work. There was no pressure at the office, and at home we found stability and comfort.

Yet something was amiss. I kept thinking about the Grateful Dead song "Uncle John's Band," with its warning that when life looks like easy street, there is danger at your door.

><><

END OF AN ERA

Periods of change, such as the year or so after an acquisition, can be turbulent. Personalities and motives may clash. Sometimes you wind up in a position with great promise, and other times you just need to move on and find a better path forward. Early in my career, with my relatively naive worldview, I had imagined that if one company acquired another, then the acquiring company took control of the acquired business. As I discovered, this is not always the case.

Relationships can be more complex. Sometimes, to convince the management team of one company to be acquired, to merge with another, there has to be some trade-off in terms of control. This may result from the acquired company feeling it needs to save face with its employees and investors, or it may occur because the two companies actually believe that the acquired company could better manage some or all of the combined business.

I also had not yet learned what would emerge as a common theme of mergers and acquisitions: these combinations are planned by a small group of senior management within the acquiring entity who don't fully understand the target business and their customers, strategy, people, or key assets. They've created some kind of story for themselves and their shareholders to justify the transaction, but that story may be based on one or more false assumptions, or incomplete information.

As a consequence there are at least five things that often happen after an acquisition:

- people in the acquired company leave (sometimes with significant wealth as a consequence of stock being cashed out);
- new people from the acquiring company are put in control who don't fully understand the business they are now running;
- a period of integration follows that is typically awkward for all, during which the combined company becomes internally focused, often at the expense of the operating business;
- the business strategy is changed in some critical manner, as new management attempts to implement their vision, which is often based on incomplete knowledge or faulty assumptions; and
- the original business suffers, sometimes temporarily, sometimes permanently.

This is not always the case. If it were, nobody would ever complete a merger. There are many acquisitions in which synergies are obvious to all, a period of integration and learning follows, redundancies are eliminated (often just a euphemism for "people are laid off"), and then the business emerges even stronger than ever.

In the case of PE/ABI, more than a year had passed since the companies had merged, and things appeared to be going well. The core business was growing nicely, and new products had been developed and launched by the merged entity. The bulk Taq and grant program for Human Genome Project centers had effectively shut down most of the bootlegging market. We were still engaged in lawsuits with a few competitors who were clearly violating our patents, but those could drag on for years.

New management decided, then, to change course and grant licenses to other companies to sell Taq DNA polymerase for use in PCR. The rationale? The environment had changed. We had effectively established our position as the market's premier supplier. By licensing major competitors, we could better monitor their performance, reduce legal fees, further strengthen our IP position, and extract a healthy royalty (which would be pure profit to us). The Perkin-Elmer sales force strongly opposed this decision, so it took an awful lot of relationship management to get everyone on board, but PE/ABI's new leadership was adamant that this would produce superior financial outcomes.

Positive developments aside, the chemistry between my immediate supervisor and me remained dysfunctional. Sometimes I'd leave a conversation clueless about what they were trying to say. I tried to make the best of things, but I knew top management wouldn't welcome me into the inner circle anytime soon. I was confused and stressed. Sooner or later someone else would be given my job. I wasn't the only one who perceived this, and rumors were flying around the office.

It all came to a head when I was informed that I was being "promoted" to vice president of business development and given a hefty raise. That was a slick move. Golden hand-cuffs. Take me out but put me in a cushy position. My oper-ational role in PE/ABI's business would be over. I was now considered part of the science and technology team, com-prising smart and upwardly mobile technology geeks ill-suited for operational responsibility, and company veterans put out to pasture. It would be a "soft landing" where I could save face, and the company wouldn't look bad for moving me, even though everyone knew how committed I was to the PCR business.

I contested the decision to no avail. I met with Riccardo Pigliucci personally to plea my case for staying at the helm of PCR. He looked me straight in the eyes and said as sin-cerely and respectfully as possible, "Stan, let me tell you something. I know how you feel. I hired you. You've done a great job for us all these years, and everyone knows it. But I have to manage this combined company now. How would it look to the rest of the organization if I vetoed their manage-ment decisions?" He paused for a moment, then delivered his final words on the topic. "Stan, I can't stop the bullet once it's left the gun."

That was it. There was nothing more to discuss. The weeks afterward were a blur. Returning to work every day was awkward, but Elise and I were not independently wealthy. We needed our jobs (for income, as well as to pursue our chosen careers). We needed time to think about how to move forward in a manner that would keep us on track.

After cooling down I realized that it wouldn't be wise to just quit. I needed to explore new opportunities and settle on an exit strategy. I couldn't seriously consider continuing my career in this organization, but surely I could learn and accomplish more to better prepare myself for the future, whatever it may be. Building up my résumé, checking off small wins, and looking for the next big thing—both for the company and for myself—became my priorities.

In my new role I lived a much slower-paced and low-key life. I got paid to review scientific papers and business plans and visit with companies developing new technologies we might want to acquire. I got to think like an entrepreneur or a venture capitalist, devising strategies for new markets the company should target for growth. I planned which types of products it would be ideal to buy or develop.

I could pitch product or business concepts to senior management if I felt one was sufficiently compelling, but just as in the venture capital world, there was usually some reason they chose not to pull the trigger and pursue an opportunity. Meanwhile the office culture was like a country club, with people arriving at any hour, taking long lunches, and making time for athletic breaks or trips to the bar. Some people might have been content to spend the rest of their career like that, but I could not.

I started applying for jobs at other companies, and as word got out into the world of recruiters, proposals started filling my inbox, and I even interviewed for a few opportunities. Many were attractive, but we needed a plan that would adequately accommodate Elise, as I couldn't leave her at ABI. Neither could I ask her to give up her job (and income!) and just follow me. Not for these run-of-the-mill jobs.

So we kept looking, and I did everything possible to maintain my professional reputation for identifying and operating cutting-edge new businesses. Now that I knew how ruthless my new superiors could be, I was determined to prevent them from labeling me negatively. I couldn't assume that simply sidelining me from the operating business would satisfy them, so I knew I had to find the next big business opportunity as soon as possible.

Over the course of six months I pulled together a plan I called the "FISH and Chips" business plan. *FISH* was the acronym for a technique called fluorescence *in situ* hybridization, which is used to analyze the locations of certain DNA sequences of interest on a chromosome, or other applications in which labeled DNA probes are hybridized to targets on solid surfaces. *Chips* was a reference to DNA microarrays, which were solid surfaces containing DNA fragments of known sequence to which labeled DNA in a sample could be hybridized. Fluorescence imaging systems could then be used to determine which of the sequences on the surface were present in the sample being analyzed. In the PCR business we had already been working with a technique called *in situ* PCR, which similarly involved imaging of labeled probes to samples on surfaces. The central idea was that by leveraging our market presence with PCR and our technological expertise in optical imaging, we could develop new systems to automate other forms of genome analysis on surfaces that could grow significantly if made more accessible to the average biologist. To be successful we needed to develop imaging systems that were small and inexpensive enough to be used by individual scientists instead of core laboratories—more personal computer than punched-card mainframe.

Strategically, this was a solid plan. The only pushback I got was a concern over doing anything with DNA arrays due to the strong IP position that others had developed around array-based analysis. That and the general reluctance to do anything new because the existing business units fought fiercely over every penny in the annual budget. They typically preferred to spend funds on their own projects rather than new ones proposed by the science and technology department.

By this time Gaynor Kelley had retired as CEO of Perkin-Elmer/ABI. Longtime Baxter employee Tony White was brought in to lead the organization, and Riccardo Pigliucci had moved on to take the helm at another life sciences company. The board, facing concerns from stockholders that the share price of good old solid Perkin-Elmer stock had been stale for too long, provided Tony with great incentives to get the share price moving up. There was a push to change the corporate image from a stodgy analytical instruments company to a rapidly growing life sciences business, capitalizing on all the buzz around biotechnology and genome sequencing. Over time the company name would be changed to PE Biosystems (and later to Applera), and efforts were initiated to find ways to unload the legacy analytical businesses and focus on high-growth life science applications.

Someone came up with an alternative to selling off some of the old businesses: taking advantage of Perkin-Elmer's core technological expertise and applying it to new systems that would interest life science customers. ABI top management was not thrilled with the idea, as they wanted to be the sole source of products for this market segment, but I saw it as an opportunity to get out of Dodge.

When volunteers were sought to pilot the project with one business unit, I jumped at the chance to lead the effort. It meant relocating to Connecticut and overseeing a business that had research and development groups in Norwalk as well as in Überlingen, Germany, a small resort town on Lake Constance (a.k.a. Bodensee). I'd get a fresh start and once again lead an operating business, but there was another key aspect to this opportunity: Elise had an offer to join the genetics department at the University of Connecticut School of Medicine in Farmington. That sealed the deal. We were heading back east.

TRANSFORMING PUF

Many hesitate to consider unconventional opportunities because of the inherent uncertainty in jobs without established career templates. There's no playbook and few, if any, mentors to rely on. These are riskier career moves, but they also provide an opportunity to be creative, to stand out from the crowd, to be recognized as a leader, and to have an impact. What's more, these opportunities arise more frequently than one who hasn't been around the block many times might assume. These are analogous to the situations an entrepreneur may encounter when establishing a new business. I was thrilled to take on this one!

The company paid for our relocation cross country, so we cleared out of the house in Half Moon Bay and headed east. Knowing Elise would be at the medical school in Farmington, we focused our home search on that area. We eventually found a remarkably affordable contemporary-style home in Avon, Connecticut, just five minutes from her lab. The only downside was my long commute, as the drive to Norwalk took ninety minutes on a good day, double that in a bad snowstorm.

The drive was worth it, though. Elise needed to be close to the lab, as she'd be working at all hours, and the house was special, sited dramatically on a bend in the Farmington River with a park reserve on the other side and a tree farm next door. Plus, I knew I would have to spend a week of every month in Germany and would be away for long stretches. It was a price I was willing to pay at that point in my career. I had the opportunity to experience many new aspects of operating a global business, even if in retrospect I hope to never experience some of those again.

I convinced several key members of the old PCR group in Norwalk to leave their tenuous long-distance relationships with ABI and come join me on the commercial side of what was now called the PUF business. We designed, developed, and sold products enabling polarimetry, ultraviolet and visible-light detection and spectroscopy, and fluorescence detection and spectroscopy. The entire group was talented, but Fenton Williams, Darren Lee, and Peter Lewis in particular played key roles in this new venture, covering support, marketing, and finance respectively. After years of working together to build the PCR business, we represented a formidable core team to start a new enterprise.

Similar to our experience with PCR, this new undertaking had the feeling of a start-up located within a multibillion-dollar global company. We were able to draw in a stellar group of engineers in Norwalk to complement the Überlingen team. Some were older folks who probably hadn't done anything interesting in a few years but were highly skilled, open to trying something new, and saw this blank piece of paper as an exciting opportunity.

Our core team shared a common vision, had worked closely together for years, trusted one another, knew our individual strengths and weaknesses, and collaborated well. Our first challenge was to identify new opportunities in the life sciences that we were prepared to address with the core technology and research-and-engineering team in Germany. This experience was similar to those I'd have later with a number of start-up companies, where you need to move beyond a high-level vision and focus instead on specific product concepts. Then you develop the information necessary to justify the investment of time and money, along with detailed plans for development and commercialization.

I started with the plans I had developed while in California as part of my "FISH and Chips" strategy. These were already well researched, justified, and documented. Perhaps as importantly, ABI had already decided not to pursue them. We focused our efforts on three of these opportunities and discontinued work on any other new products at the German site, known as BSW, for Bodenseewerk.

We first aimed to develop a fluorescence imaging system for slide-based microarrays. ABI didn't want to pursue this project due to IP issues, but we thought there was room for a product here and that licensing was possible if truly necessary. The difference of opinion created some internal controversy, but the project excited the German team. They had innovative design ideas and thought they could use the program to revitalize their business. Rumors circulated that top management was unhappy with the cost of operating in Germany and hesitant to start new programs, so the German team was thrilled to have this opportunity.

Our second program was to create a small benchtop "personal" spectrophotometer, which came to be called the MBA 2000. Designed to be the size of a shoebox so as to take up little benchtop space in the lab, the instrument had no moving parts and an intuitive touch screen graphic user interface enabling the operator to run applications typically used in life science research. This was my favorite project, a complete no-brainer in my view, and quite novel in many respects. None of our targeted applications needed high-precision analytical performance. This was completely mind boggling to our engineers, who were accustomed to seeking higher and higher performance. Instead, size, dedicated life science apps, and ease of use were the goals! And low cost so we could sell at a low price.

One of my key marketing design requirements for the MBA 2000 was that it would have no moving parts. The old-timer Perkin-Elmer engineers insisted it couldn't be done. We had to have a fan to cool the system or it would over-heat. I kept pushing and, at some point, suggested simply adding vents on top, right over the electronics board. They all agreed that should provide sufficient cooling, but then wondered aloud, "Could the instrument pass the water test?" What was the water test?!

There is a standard instrument design protocol that requires a measured amount of water—a cup?—to be poured atop the instrument and not affect its performance. The engineers came up with an idea to shield the electronics to divert incoming water but leave an open layer on all sides so that heat could escape and then go up through the vents. And it worked!

The key component that made such a design possible was a small solid-state spectrophotometer device manufactured by Ocean Optics. It was originally designed to sit on the end of a long cable submerged into seawater to measure the light spectra at different depths. Fenton had brought this tiny spectrophotometer to our attention, and we wanted to incorporate it into our own box even though it was manufactured by another company. We needed to go meet them, see the product and their manufacturing operation, and discuss a potential relationship.

Ocean Optics was located in a small building a block off the beach in Dunedin, Florida. For our first visit, we asked about the dress code in advance and were advised that their only requirement was we wear shoes. By sheer coincidence, we visited on the first day of stone crab season. When the presentations, factory tour, and discussions were complete, we walked to a beachside bar. They couldn't legally serve stone crabs until midnight, so we spent the evening drinking Beck's beers and trading stories until the clock struck twelve. Then waiters emerged from the kitchen with trays overflowing with freshly steamed stone crabs. The night was long, but we became great friends. The MBA 2000 would go on to be a breakthrough instrument and inspire many followers who launched products that incorporated various aspects of our design.

The third and final program was a ninety-six-well microplate plate reader that could measure light in different wavelengths and in different modes. We wanted a single instrument that could measure both light absorption in the ultraviolet-visible-wavelength range as well as fluorescence and chemiluminescence. This would make the system useful in a wide range of life science applications and enable scientists to replace multiple instruments with one, thereby saving costs and benchtop space. Darren led the project, and he had contacts at a company called SLT in Salzburg, Austria, who were working on an instrument that could do just what we needed.

The project turned out to be controversial. PE's ABI division had just acquired a company for access to their proprietary chemiluminescence technology. To use this technology, customers needed plate readers similar to the one we were developing with SLT. Of course, those leading the project at ABI wanted to make the plate readers themselves.

You can probably see where this is all going. Some in ABI started lobbying for us to terminate the SLT relationship and discontinue the plate reader, rather than working together—as if we were indeed one company—and simply selling their new reagents for use with our plate reader. I was going to have a fight on my hands, but I was determined to turn the old PUF business into a state-of-the-art life science operation and make a big impact with our new products.

✕✕✕

SHUTDOWN

While on a trip to BSW we got word that an all-company meeting had been set for the next morning, and that senior Perkin-Elmer officials from the States would be speaking—about what, we had no idea. A few of us from the US made sure to arrive early and sit in the front row. A crowd of at least five hundred employees sat behind us, jammed into a large cafeteria that also served as an auditorium. Atop a makeshift stage sat a lectern and a table with a few folding chairs. As the crowd filed in, the dignitaries, including the German site manager and a few human resources reps for both Überlingen and Norwalk, made their way to the stage.

The site manager called the meeting to order and introduced the executives, infrequent visitors who had never spoken to all the BSW employees as a group. An executive stepped up to the lectern to speak. Imagine a tall blond woman wearing a designer dress and expensive gold jewelry. After a few pleasantries delivered with a thick Boston accent, she got right to the point.

"As you all know, we sell our products all over the world, and we make them in a variety of countries around the globe. It should be no surprise to anyone in this room that the tax rate is high in Germany, and the cost of living here is high. That wouldn't matter if the people who worked here were more productive than those in other places, or more efficient, or could buy components at lower costs—but none of those things are true. The simple fact is that if we continue to make products at this location, we will have a substantially higher cost than our competitors. In order to continue competing, we will either have to reduce our costs so that we can maintain market share with adequate profits or increase our prices. If we increase prices, we will likely lose market share, and we've exhausted our efforts at trying to reduce costs."

You could hear a pin drop in the room.

"So we've made the difficult decision to close this site," she continued, "and to move manufacturing of all BSW products to other sites around the world that operate with a lower cost structure. We'll do our best to find jobs for those of you who want to relocate to those other sites, but we can't guarantee we will have jobs for all of you even if you want to move. I know this is not good news, but you have nobody to blame but yourselves. It's our job to be responsible for the best interests of the company as a whole, and if we can't be competitive operating here in Germany, then we have no choice but to leave."

The crowd was stunned. So was I. Some of us had concerns about BSW, but nobody seriously thought the site would be shuttered. Aside from its worldwide renown for product excellence and quality, Perkin-Elmer was a model of stability. BSW had been producing world-class instruments since the end of the Second World War. People worked there for life. They took care of employees as if they were family. The notion that this site would be closed to make the company more profitable and increase its public share price was unimaginable to most who worked there. They couldn't comprehend this new way of working in a global economy where top management was judged and rewarded on share-price performance.

There was silence at first, and I was afraid to turn around and eye the crowd. Then one man stood up in the back and started talking. Clearly nervous, he shifted between English and German. He spoke of the long history of operations in Überlingen, a company reputation built on the backs of hardworking engineers, and on and on. His voice grew shaky until he finally started talking loudly in German exclusively, and though I didn't understand the words, I knew he was cursing.

Nearby colleagues intervened and managed to get him to stop talking and sit down. A few queries about logistics followed, but after the second answer the well-dressed executive made her exit, telling the crowd that the others onstage were better qualified to address their concerns. The decision had been made, and there was no debating it.

Going to my meetings that day was out of the question. I had to decide which people in my German operation I would try to save. By *save* I meant finding a role for them in Connecticut and hoping I could make them a satisfactory offer to relocate. I made my way back to the hotel and had a quiet night in my room. I couldn't imagine walking into one of the pubs in town where the factory workers were surely gathered. I got a ride to the airport in Zurich first thing in the morning.

Convincing employees to relocate, or letting them go—even for employees long considered "excess baggage"—was one of the most difficult and depressing activities of my career. Indeed, a few had not made significant contributions in years, while enjoying high salaries, good benefits, and perks such as sailing at lunchtime. Nonetheless, they were not bad people, they still had families to support, and finding other local employment would be difficult. I felt like I was back in graduate school, cutting off rat heads. Some greater good was being served, presumably, but I never wanted to do this again. Once I survived this experience I was convinced that, as much as possible, I would try to be involved in growth situations in the future.

It also left a bad taste in my mouth of the brutal realities of life in a big multinational public company where senior management focused on doing anything necessary to drive up stock prices and maximize the value of top-executive equity compensation. The shutdown of BSW was a rude awakening for me, revealing at a personal level the impact of living in a world in which shareholder profits, executive compensation, and the value of a share of stock mattered above all else.

It was one of the uglier sides of our capitalist system, especially given the associated impact this practice has had on soaring degrees of income inequality. If getting removed from my leadership role in PCR was the first strike against a career at Perkin-Elmer, then living through this experience was the second. I was one step closer to a major change in career direction.

The next few months were a low point in my career. All three of my product development programs were going well, and the core PUF business based on the legacy products was performing as expected (albeit with low expectations). Still, most of my time was tied up dealing with human resources issues related to the staff in Germany. Some would be terminated, and others relocated to Connecticut. I helped some of them find new jobs elsewhere. I hated all of it.

As if dealing with the BSW shutdown wasn't bad enough, all three of my programs eventually started to get serious pushback. Not everyone agreed that this business-unit-refocusing experiment was worthwhile. Some had lobbied to shut down the old analytical instruments business entirely or sell it off and use the resulting cash to finance the life science businesses based in California. The prospect of us introducing cutting-edge life science products from another division, some felt, would create confusion in the minds of customers as to who they should call for service and support.

Once again I felt as if I were drowning. A year spent shutting down a business in a foreign country, terminating employees, and living in a bureaucratic and political nightmare—it was all too much. But I stayed close with my PUF team. We were the Magnificent Seven on a mission to save the world for the good of all humanity ("Justice has a number"). The final straw broke, however, when a reorganization was announced and a sales manager with no knowledge of our business became my new superior. I was tired of all this and, once again, sensed progress delayed and fun denied.

Recruiters had been calling me regularly. They almost always started with "Hey, Stan, you wouldn't happen to know someone who has the following capabilities . . ." Then they'd share a list of capabilities that was a dead-on description of me.

One day, instead of saying "Let me think about that and get back to you," I said, "Tell me more." And one day not too much later, the right opportunity appeared.

6

ENTREPRENEURSHIP AND DNA ANALYSIS

GENETIC MICROSYSTEMS START-UP

At forty-one years old I had spent the past fifteen years transitioning from a naive PhD graduate to a seasoned business professional. I now understood how to find new product ideas, justify them to financial backers (from NIH to internal boards), and build, manage, and grow them into successful global businesses with revenue exceeding $100 million annually and valuations five to ten times that high. I'd been exposed to the world of mergers and acquisitions, and to IPOs and life as an employee of a public company.

I had also seen enough big-company politics and bureaucracy to know that I had no interest in continuing to climb the corporate ladder. It was time for me to venture out on my own, to either become CEO of an existing small company or perhaps found a new one myself. I needed to find something I was passionate about, where I could put my skills to good use and convince coworkers and investors to join me on a worthy mission. Dave Nelson's words from a chance meeting a year earlier at a scientific conference still haunted me. "Those days working with PCR were really special," he said. "You'll never have that much fun in business again." I was determined to prove Dave wrong.

A fellow we'll call "Tyler," a successful serial entrepreneur and financier from San Diego, had relocated to Toronto and was building a portfolio of new biotech companies in Canada. Tyler had raised funds from Canadian venture capital firms and obtained substantial support from the Canadian government. One of these businesses was a molecular biology reagents company. The operations aspect of the business was nearly a carbon copy of what I had managed back at Perkin-Elmer Cetus but without rights to PCR.

It would never be worth as much as the PCR franchise, but as CEO I'd have an equity stake and the opportunity to reap a much larger reward on a successful outcome than I could if I were merely a salaried employee. What's more, I could choose on which areas to focus the talented research, development, and commercial teams. Surely I could find an exciting emerging application area where we could have an impact and take a leadership position. I could do this job in my sleep, and the opportunity might yield something truly exciting, even if the current business was fairly mundane.

Elise and I flew to Toronto in late June, around the time of the city's annual jazz festival. I had been to Toronto once before, during college, when a few friends and I drove up from Ithaca, crossing the border at Niagara Falls after a brief pit stop to make sure there was no weed remaining in the car. We spent forty-eight hours at a friend of a friend's house party, drinking Labatt Blues, smoking, dancing, and meeting new people. I might have slept for an hour here or there on a random couch.

This time was much different. Tyler put us up in a hotel suite at the Fairmont Royal York, just a few blocks from Lake Ontario. He took us to Barberian's Steakhouse, where we dined on enormous slabs of beef, perfectly grilled. Then back to his downtown home, which took up an entire four-story building. Decorated with Oriental rugs, fine French antiques, and awards from his daughter's swimming competitions, it was all very attractive. What's more, the price of real estate was a fraction of that in Boston or San Francisco. We could live well here.

The next morning Tyler and his wife drove us around town in his gold Mercedes SL500 convertible and showed us different neighborhoods. We also stopped by the office so I could see exactly what I was getting into. It was technically in Mississauga, a neighboring city where many businesses had set up shop in a low-rent district closer to the airport. The labs and offices seemed well equipped. Upon seeing what appeared to be an original abstract painting based on Leonardo da Vinci's *Vitruvian Man* hanging in Tyler's office, Elise exclaimed, "That's incredible. I wish I had one of those."

"You could never afford it," Tyler replied.

With that we left for brunch. Apart from Tyler's condescending remark about the artwork, things were going well, and I was getting comfortable with the idea that this could be a good spot for a fresh start. After all the eggs and Canadian bacon we could handle, Tyler put the top down on his Mercedes and drove us to the airport. At some point he picked up a pencil, stuck it in his ear, and started flicking out hunks of ear wax that blew back with the wind and hit Elise in the face. It was all downhill from there.

The entire flight home all I heard about was what a disgusting slob that man was. A slick salesman trying to convince me to leave the country and take the helm at some backwater company nobody had ever heard of. Sure, Elise would likely get a position at the University of Toronto, but were things really that bad? Was this really my best option? It might be easy, but it seemed like a big step down from where I had been.

There was, in fact, one other option. Jean "Coco" Montagu, the founder and former CEO of General Scanning (GSI), had invited me to meet with him the following Sunday at his home on a secluded, tree-lined street in Brookline, Massachusetts. Coco had heard through the rumor mill that I was frustrated at Perkin-Elmer. He could relate, as he had recently resigned as GSI's CEO, partly out of frustration with the company's new board and their focus on cost cutting rather than innovation. Coco had an idea for a new company, and he wondered whether I might be interested in joining him.

Coco's wife, Kyra, had prepared a light lunch for the three of us, after which Coco and I moved from the kitchen to the back porch, where we spent the rest of the afternoon drinking wine, sharing personal stories, and considering the opportunity. The company would focus on developing and commercializing systems for capturing high-resolution digital images of DNA spots on surfaces arranged in ordered patterns, or arrays. I understood the opportunity well, as I had independently prepared and pitched to ABI a business plan for this same opportunity (without having access to Coco's technology) over a year earlier.

Coco's idea was brilliant: a new type of imaging system superior to anything on the market, built at a fraction of the cost. What Coco didn't know was how to reach the right customers and effectively commercialize such products, which happened to be my specialty and passion. I was thrilled!

I learned more about Coco's frustration and exhaustion from dealing with corporate politics too. He had founded GSI, grown the business with a series of innovations leading to new product opportunities, and taken the company public. Over time, however, he found himself isolated with a group working on new applications but a board that didn't support any of them. Coco enjoyed working in the "sandbox," but the board's preferences began to diverge from his own, and he slowly became more and more isolated.

Eventually Coco had had enough. He resigned, cashed in some of his stock (worth several hundred million dollars), and set out to start a new company doing the things he felt were really important. I may not have had the resources or the accomplishments that Coco did, but we were of a like mind when it came to big-company politics and passion projects. We needed each other, and we both carried chips on our shoulders. We were out to prove others wrong and make a big impact.

Coco and I connected in a strong and personal way that afternoon, and we came away feeling pretty good about the idea. We had confidence and trust in each other's capabilities and excellent personal chemistry from the moment we met. We agreed to go forward as partners in a new company we decided to name Genetic MicroSystems. We just needed to work out a few details, such as equity distribution and compensation, before I could quit my job at Perkin-Elmer.

I had little experience with stock ownership at this point in my life. With no idea how much equity to ask Coco for, or how to think about compensation in this situation, I called my uncle, Pete, the only family member who had actually started and sold a company. After explaining the situation to him, Pete advised me to ask for three things: a contract guaranteeing me a salary for two years at a level somewhat above what I was making at Perkin-Elmer, 10 percent of the founders stock, and antidilution protection on my 10 percent.

Coco was amenable to most of this. In his view, 50 percent of the equity should go to the investors and 50 percent to the workers. Of the workers' 50 percent, I'd get 10. We'd eventually come back to thinking about how to split the other 40 percent, but that needn't be solved immediately. We never discussed future stock options, or a stock option pool in general, at least not until the lawyers brought it to our attention.

We agreed that Coco would be CEO and responsible for financing and engineering, and I would be chief operating officer and focused primarily on marketing and all aspects of commercialization. The initial financing would be $3 million, two-thirds of which came from reinvestment of proceeds from Coco's sale of GSI stock and the rest from Coco's friends. He could easily have funded it all himself, but he reasoned that it would probably be unwise to proceed if he couldn't convince a few wealthy friends to invest.

The antidilution protection that Uncle Pete suggested I

request was a favorable term for me but a big headache ulti-mately. I was too new at all this to understand why Coco and others were opposed to it. Bob Johnson, our third founding board member, tried to explain it to me. "Look, Stan, it's not that we don't want you to have it. The problem is that no VC will ever invest in us if anyone has that kind of protection. If we can't raise money, the company will fail, so it's just not a good idea." He was obviously right, but I didn't have the experience to know, so we politely debated this point for around a month.

Eventually Bob proposed a creative alternative. "How about we provide you with limited antidilution protection through the first $10 million of financing? That will likely come from other angels who won't care, especially if they know it's going away by the time we need to raise big VC money. Also, bear in mind that we can always award you ad-ditional stock options going forward based on performance. This will help counter the effects of dilution from taking new investments."

I trusted them. I was convinced. It was a great solution.

In September 1997 I quit Perkin-Elmer and we formally founded Genetic MicroSystems, working out of Coco's basement. I love being able to tell people that my first start-up was in a basement. Truthfully, it was some of the nicest office space in which I've ever worked: a large open area, a separate machine shop off to one side, and an amaz-ing art collection that included sculptures and paintings. Every morning Coco brewed strong coffee for us and ran to a local French bakery for croissants. We had one big center table for group conversations and a few desks spread around to provide individual workspaces. The parklike backyard setting was ideal for taking breaks when weather permitted. The energy in that room was incredibly strong and motivating. We had assembled a small group of five or six people to start, including a few consultants Coco had known for years, and we were truly on a mission. It was just what I always imagined start-up life would be like.

As the business began to feel more "real," Elise quit her academic position at the University of Connecticut School of Medicine and agreed to join in our effort by setting up a small biological laboratory where we could test products in development. We relocated to the town of Boxford on Boston's north shore, buying an old farmhouse with a barn on six acres. Shortly after moving in, we walked to our nearest neighbor's place to introduce ourselves. We knocked and were greeted by a pleasant-enough couple who promptly invited us inside.

After exchanging names, the wife, making friendly conversation, asked, "So what do you do for a living?"

"I'm cofounder of a start-up biotech company," I replied. There was no sense getting any more detailed than that.

The husband quickly shot back: "Oh, a start-up! Those are pretty risky, aren't they?"

I thought for a second and looked him in the eye. "I guess that depends on your sense of risk. From my perspective, at a big company with thousands of people, where you never know what the executives up on Mahogany Row are thinking, you might receive a pink slip on any given day because they decide they need to cut costs so they can hit their quarterly profit targets and receive bonuses. Now that's risky. But having two years' guaranteed salary, a healthy chunk of stock, and a chance to work with a group of people of my own choosing, on a project I'm excited about—where success or failure depends on my efforts and those of the people I choose to be on my team. . . . Well, I'll take that bet any day."

Soon thereafter Elise surprised me one afternoon when I came home to find two adorable black puppies that were a Labrador–German shepherd mix. We named the male Rowley for the town where he was born, and the female Trinka in memory of our friend's dog we had fallen in love with while house-sitting in California. These two litter-mates provided unwavering love, comfort, and joy during a period when I would be working as hard as I can remember. I would never be without dogs in my life again.

The path that led me to this job was unplanned and could not have been predicted in advance. If I hadn't been forced out of my comfort zone in the PCR business, I never would have even met Coco! I had been sideswiped by a completely unexpected event and had faced a potentially career-ending challenge, yet I never gave up on my longer-term goals. It took patience, persistence, and resilience, but I was consumed with this new venture, and the thought of failure never crossed my mind.

For me and Coco it all started with a shared vision, common values, and great personal chemistry. Now we were off and running. My decision not to move to Canada and instead join Coco felt validated a few months later when a terrible ice storm hit Toronto, knocking out power for two weeks as people endured temperatures twenty degrees below zero Fahrenheit. The city—and Tyler's company, presumably—was shut down, but here in Boston we were just getting started.

✕✕✕

THE TOILET PAPER TEST

Among Coco Montagu's many special qualities was an incredible talent for rapidly identifying whether an idea for a new invention might actually work. As most know, or should know, time is our most precious resource. The ability to make the best use of one's time is thus an incredible gift. Coco once told me, "One of my real talents is that I can get you 90 percent of the way to the right answer, really fast. I'll absolutely have the wrong answer, mind you, but I'll be really close really fast, so we can figure out whether the approach is worth pursuing."

I'd later come to learn that a whole field of rapid prototyping existed based on this approach to problems. The notion of building the minimum viable product follows from the same way of thinking. This is critical to any early-stage business trying to move fast, conserve cash, and determine whether a new product concept solves a customer's problem and offers a competitive advantage. It's also an invaluable approach for quickly detecting events you may never have anticipated.

The "toilet paper test," a real turning point for Genetic MicroSystems, is a case in point. We had formed a company with the primary goal of making laser scanning digital imaging systems for analyzing "do-it-yourself DNA microarrays." Our dilemma? These microarrays were essentially microscope slides with tiny spots of DNA placed on them in regular patterns, but early on we realized that if we couldn't provide a way for our customers to manufacture their own DNA microarrays, they'd have no need for the array scanners we were planning to develop. Additionally, every known approach to making a DNA microarray seemed to be covered by patents owned by competitors with no interest in licensing us or enabling customers to make arrays of their own design.

Coco used other people's patents as sources of ideas more than anyone I've ever met, and this was just one of many valuable lessons I learned from him. He was a masterful reader and writer of patents. In this case there were patents covering the idea of creating capillaries in tubes that one would bring into contact with a surface repeatedly to make ordered arrays of spots on a surface. There were various approaches to synthesizing arrays *in situ*, generally using photolabile chemistry and photolithographic masks. There were inkjet-printing-type approaches to blow a spot onto a surface. All were described in patents, and our path forward appeared to be blocked. But not so fast!

Coco had an idea. He called everyone present that day over to the conference table, and we all pulled up our chairs. On the table he laid out several pieces of toilet paper and opened a container of india ink. For those too young to know, this was a dark indigo-blue ink that usually came in thick glass bottles.

In the days before the ballpoint, a pen that was used to write on paper was a simple device that relied on capillary action drawing fluid up into a hollow tube. The tubular structure could have been inside or attached to any long linear object, such as a stick, a piece of metal, or a bird feather. The pen's tube generally had a thin segment extending from the tip up to an area that was larger in volume and could act as a reservoir. One would dip the pen into a container of india ink, which would be drawn up the gap by capillary action and fill the tube and reservoir. Then you could write or draw by virtue of the ink flowing from the pen when the tip was moved across the paper's fibrous surface. If you looked closely, you'd see that the ink spread a certain distance from the tip of the pen, which was dependent on factors such as the blotting capacity of the paper, the viscosity of the ink, the width of the gap in the pen's tip, and the pressure applied by the writer.

In his demonstration, Coco pulled out a paper clip and untwisted it to form a long, almost straight rod of metal with a flat end. He dipped the end into the india ink, raised it up, and noticed that a small hemisphere of the liquid clung to the bottom tip of the clip by surface tension. He carefully touched the droplet of ink that hung from the metal to the toilet paper, and the deep blue ink quickly transferred from the pin to the paper without the metal ever making contact. The ink then spread out in all directions, forming a perfect circle. Coco repeated the process, and voilà! Another perfect circle formed on the toilet paper, with exactly the same dimensions as the first one.

We didn't take precise measurements, but it was obvious that the spots were the same size and that the amount of liquid transferred to the surface was about the same volume. Coco repeated this several more times with the same result, and smiles broke out. We all realized Coco had conceived and demonstrated a new way of making spots on surfaces that did not involve capillaries, contact, jetting, or synthesis—a new way not covered by any issued patents!

Much more work was required to turn this into an actual DNA-printing device. Different materials were evaluated. Different-size pins were tested. An elegant approach was conceived to automate the printing process and create a moving reservoir to repeatedly refill the tip of the pin. But the concept had been proved, and from that point on, we knew we were in business. That piece of toilet paper went into the lab notebook, was signed and dated, and served as the basis of several invention disclosures written and filed with the help of our patent lawyer. Eventually a patent application would be filed, and a few years later a US patent would issue.

Hence was born the "pin and ring technology," which became the basis for our first product, the GMS 417 DNA Arrayer. The model number 417 was chosen because Coco had signed a noncompetition agreement with General Scanning that prohibited him from working on DNA array fluorescence imaging systems until after April 17, 1998, but that said nothing about spotting systems. Just another example of Coco's playfulness. Our first imaging system was of course named the GMS 418 Array Scanner because it was the first product we could make beginning April 18.

There's a beauty to this story that I didn't appreciate until, while lounging in Coco's living room, I noticed his collection of wire sculptures. He must have enjoyed the fact he had invented this breakthrough technology, which circumvented the patent blockade created by the field's greatest legal and scientific minds, by twisting wires for fun, by three-dimensional doodling.

It wasn't always easy working with Coco. His stories

were captivating, and his jokes were fun—as long as you weren't the butt of them. You had to get used to his broken English and French accent, as well as his dyslexia, which often appeared verbally or in writing at times that seemed particularly convenient for him. Maybe that was just a coincidence. He could be stubborn. I never really fought with him, but I saw a few disagreements with others, and in each case he gave them a hard time about it. As a PhD biologist, I was annoyed to no end when he told GMS visitors that the scientists work on one side of the building, the biologists on the other. It probably takes a biologist to appreciate the joke.

Challenges with Coco are easily forgiven and almost forgotten once I think about what made him so special. He was strong willed, loyal, intelligent, creative, and driven by the quest for knowledge. He was warm, caring, and comforting. He was passionate about his work and applied himself to the tasks at hand as hard as anyone I've ever known. At the same time, he understood the importance of fun, humor, and the celebration of our achievements, even the small ones. He enjoyed working at the bench, and no task was beneath him. Cleaning dishes or taking out the garbage was something we all had to do, no matter our title. I appreciated Coco's sense of fairness too. He was a near-perfect business partner and a trusted friend. Looking back on it over twenty years later, I'm grateful for how fortunate I was to have shared my first pure start-up journey with him, and what a unique experience it was.

✕✕✕

THE TAKARA DEAL

The need to move fast and to appreciate the time-value of money were pressures Coco and I felt intuitively. Anyone watching us slowly filter into the basement office each morning or leisurely chat over strong coffee and freshly baked croissants might have thought otherwise. We avoided making sloppy mistakes in haste, but we possessed a sense of urgency. We had developed a formal schedule, but we were always racing to accomplish things faster than that, and I think this was one of our great advantages as a start-up. We were careful not to burn through cash too quickly, but we also knew we were onto a good idea and it wouldn't be long before fast followers would appear.

Six months into our new business we had already established our core team and were well on our way to completing the spotter and scanner designs. By March 1998 we were ready to move out of the basement. We felt we needed roughly 1,500 square feet of raw space that could be split into an office and lab/workshop, ideally with a loading dock.

We focused our search halfway between Boxford to the north and Brookline to the south and found several possible office sites in the town of Woburn, at the intersection of Routes 95 and 93. This was a great location for start-up companies, and a whole ecosystem of related service businesses had opened in the area, from office-supply stores to restaurants and hotels. Access was easy from all directions, and rent was 50 percent less than what we'd have to pay in Kendall Square, the big biotech hub emerging in Cambridge.

We kept our search efficient, looking at only three sites before choosing one. Thankfully Coco had done this before, as I still had a lot to learn about picking raw space. You had to have a vision for what it could be transformed into, and Coco could see this more clearly than could I. We signed a lease and quickly went about moving in. As with a new home, the moving in was exciting but frustrating too. Packing and lifting boxes isn't much fun, but there is a certain joy in unpacking those boxes, putting your mark on the walls, and creating an environment where great things could happen.

Unlike in the basement in Brookline, in the new space we needed a receptionist and support person. We advertised in a local newspaper, and the first person we interviewed was a young woman named Jessica. Amid more unpacking, Coco and I each spent twenty minutes or so speaking with her, and once we compared notes, we agreed she could handle the job. We had no interest in interviewing another candidate. Back to unpacking.

We realized we had passed that critical juncture where we needed to hire more people in order to effectively execute our plans. More people meant we needed to raise more money. I had given little thought to fundraising, as Coco had easily pulled together the initial funding and promised me a two-year commitment. I imagined he could go back to the same well of high-net-worth individuals and ask for more, but Coco felt that broadening the syndicate would give him comfort that we were on the right track and signal strength to the outside world. He also wanted to see that a group with experience in the industry valued what we had created and our vision for the future.

Coco, Bob Johnson, and I met to discuss the next round of funding, including how much to raise, what we hoped to accomplish with the funds, and who we knew that might be interested in investing and at what valuation. As we thought about whom we might approach, I suggested, "What about selling distribution rights to our future products in a territory that we are never likely to address on our own anyway?"

More specifically, I was thinking about Japan. During my days managing the PCR business for Perkin-Elmer and Applied Biosystems, I had become quite close to our Japanese partner, Takara Shuzo. My personal contact at Takara was their biotechnology guru and board member Dr. Ikunoshin Kato. We had a trusting relationship, and I had become familiar enough with how product distribution and sales worked in Japan to know that our new little company was many years away from being able to address this on our own.

Coco, Bob, and I discussed this approach and agreed it could make a lot of sense. What's more, such an investment might be structured so as to be nondilutive. We could sell them distribution rights without giving up any stock, or perhaps only provide warrants that could be converted to stock in the future. In either case, the deal would have greater public relations value than simply raising more funds from angel investors and would demonstrate to the outside world that an established life sciences company wanted to distribute our products.

I contacted Kato-san, updated him on my new business, and asked if he would be in the Boston area anytime soon so that we might show him what was happening at GMS. He rapidly replied that he was interested in the whole field of array-based analysis and was visiting the US once a month. He would be delighted to meet us.

By the time Kato-san arrived, accompanied by his younger head of business development, we had the office and the workshop area all set up, had hired three or four more people, and looked like a real-life start-up. The office was buzzing every day. Equipment was running, software engineers were writing code, music was playing loudly from a boom box, and the mechanical engineers were busy constructing, wiring, and testing parts.

Jessica was all set up at a reception desk. A whiteboard hung on the flimsy wood-paneled walls of our small conference room. We'd sourced the furniture from a second-hand dealer who resold at a fraction of the new retail price anything you needed from companies that had gone out of business. We were clearly cost conscious.

Coco and I both wore white shirts and ties out of respect for our visitors. We gathered in the conference room, served strong Peet's coffee to all, and presented our six-month-old pitch deck, followed by a tour of "the lab." We shared our respective backgrounds and our vision for the future. Having known me for eight years now, Kato-san could tell right away that we were onto something and that this was too good of an opportunity to pass up.

"How much money do you need?" he asked politely.

"Three million dollars will get us past the initial run of beta systems," we explained, "which will be sufficiently advanced that we can place them in customer labs and likely get paid for them. Those will be done by the end of the year."

A fast timetable. We were talking about going from start-up and product concepts to delivered functioning units in less than fifteen months. Perkin-Elmer engineers would insist that this couldn't be done in less than eighteen months.

Kato-san could see from the lab's activity that we were well on our way. After further discussion, mostly focused on whether $3 million was enough, we agreed that Takara would invest $3 million in exchange for rights to distribute in Japan, South Korea, China, and Taiwan, along with warrants to purchase 5 percent of the company's stock in five years at the current price per share for common stock (next to nothing). This gave them a tangible asset they could book and a significant upside in the deal, and cost us little.

We also agreed to place our first eight beta prototypes in Japan, which would be paid for at a preagreed transfer price. The sooner we could deliver, the sooner we could book revenue, which was a great motivator for our team. Supporting our first eight instruments on the other side of the world was less than ideal, but having them all go to one point of contact was helpful. Now, aside from just funding, we had a high-profile Japanese partnership we could announce in a press release, an internal goal for production, a means for obtaining great early feedback from beta site customers in Japan, and early sales momentum. And we had given up no current equity in the company.

We did in fact go on to deliver those instruments as planned, and the fast timeline satisfied me after so many years of hearing that things just couldn't be done that quickly. To celebrate the success of this relationship, Elise and I, along with our vice president of sales, Greg McGuinness, traveled to Kyoto to visit with Takara in early 1999. They arranged for us to stay in a traditional Japanese inn where guests were served rice tea at reception, slept on futon mattresses on the floor, bathed in deep Japanese tubs, and had meals served in private tatami rooms with bamboo screens overlooking meticulous Japanese gardens with koi ponds, bonsai trees, and stone walkways.

It seemed like a dream, but it was a dream come true. We could never have expected to be sitting there back in the fall of 1997. To a large degree our success depended on the strong foundations we had developed, our planning and persistence in pushing to move quickly in executing those plans, our creativity in thinking about how to finance our growth, and our leveraging of long-term relationships in ways that benefited everyone involved.

QUEST FOR THREE HUNDRED

Transitioning from a research and development organization with a bold vision to a true commercial organization capable of manufacturing, marketing, and selling is a big milestone in the life of a start-up. At GMS we now needed to expand the organization and begin evaluating new metrics that were less about technical accomplishment and more about getting and keeping customers and generating revenue. During this period many issues were encountered for the first time, some completely unexpected and all needing to be addressed ASAP.

I was handling most of the marketing—strategic and tactical—and overseeing the customer-facing aspects of our operation. Nick Mace, one of Coco's associates from his days at General Scanning, was focused on business development and finding potential partners and collaborators interested in our products. I brought in Greg McGuinness to lead sales. Pete Lewis transitioned from a part-time consultant to a full-time employee handling finance and built a team and infrastructure to handle the operation's accounting and financial aspects.

Mike Ryan was hired to create a first-class manufacturing operation in what had formerly been an empty mannequin factory. Mike was a McKinsey-trained fellow whose last gig had been putting in place manufacturing for the Bose Wave Radio. We had some concerns about whether he was a good fit since our systems were more complex, higher priced, and would be built in significantly lower volumes than a consumer electronics device. As it turned out, Mike was perfectly suited for the task. By the end of 1998 we had delivered on the first eight prototypes we had promised Takara and were well on our way to scaling up production.

Phil Officer had been hired as a one-man band to handle worldwide service. The Japanese installations were all done by phone and were handled without incident, save one. Nothing Phil could say over the phone seemed to solve the problem, so he flew overnight to Japan. Bleary-eyed after the thirteen-hour flight, he went straight to the university lab to address the issue. Within five minutes he discovered that the instrument end of the power cord had come loose. The local representatives had checked that the cord was plugged into the wall, but not into the instrument! He raced back to Narita and caught the first flight back to Boston, having flown round trip across the Pacific in less than forty-eight hours for a five-minute job.

Greg had joined us earlier in 1998 with a ton of enthusiasm, not to mention an impressive network developed over the prior decade as the top performing sales representative and field application specialist, first for Perkin-Elmer's PCR business and later for Stratagene's molecular cloning systems. Greg understood he would be on the front lines selling our systems, but now he would have the added responsibility of building and managing a sales team. He knew all our KOL customers across the country and a ton of fellow sales representatives he might recruit.

In short order Greg cherry-picked some of the top performing sales reps and support specialists, all of whom understood the opportunity we were addressing, trusted our leadership team, and were eager to sell our instruments. Going into our first full year of product sales, we huddled and came up with a plan. We set a target for selling three hundred instruments at $50,000 apiece, for a first-year goal of $15 million in revenue.

These numbers were ambitious by most standards, but we knew the market, we knew the void our products were designed to fill, we knew how much better they were than any alternatives, and we knew we had experienced people selling for us who brought strong relationships with KOL customers. What's more, we had Takara primed to drive our products into Japan, South Korea, China, and Taiwan. The one thing we didn't yet have was a strong European sales network, but Greg was confident he could pull this together quickly. From the production side, Mike kept telling us that he could handle any number we threw at him, and that we couldn't sell systems fast enough to cause a problem. I prayed he was right.

With all the hiring we had planned, I knew we would need help in recruiting, interviewing, and onboarding new people. I also knew that when any team gets large enough (somewhere between two and ten people), you're bound to run into unanticipated human resources issues. These may range from people simply not getting along to outright discrimination or harassment. Real or perceived, it's still a problem that must be addressed. In human resources parlance they refer to this as "employee relations."

I felt strongly that our employees should all have equity in the company, and industry comparable/leading benefit packages, and that we should do whatever we could afford to help them develop their career paths. We didn't have enough cash to offer them all the highest-possible salaries, but they were all fairly compensated. With only a dozen or so employees hired, a former colleague referred me to a seasoned HR professional whom we hired to take care of all these issues. Few things are as important as the people you hire, and your personal network can only take you so far.

We put a lot of effort into strategic planning and defining our product-market fit and desired positioning. We created a messaging statement and image package that would become associated with our brand. Once again I called on Lena Chow for assistance. I had worked on many advertising campaigns by now, but this one was the first for my own company. I paid extra-close attention to the details around logo design and choice of fonts, colors, and shapes. Together we mapped out an aggressive advertising campaign and related promotional activities. We would joke internally that Lena and her team were too expensive for us, but everything they produced was first class, and they were a joy to work with.

We came up with the tagline "Changing the image of DNA microarrays." Lena's team worked with a vague concept I had about enabling analysis of DNA in new, improved ways that would yield fresh insights. After a bit of brainstorming, they created an unforgettable key graphic element for use in marketing materials. It reminded me of the Rick Griffin flying-eyeball psychedelic posters promoting the Jimi Hendrix Experience in the late 1960s. Our version had pieces of DNA emanating from the eye. Sticking with the Hendrix metaphor, our systems would provide users with a new experience.

We leveraged relationships with our scientific advisors to place our first beta units in the US, get data developed demonstrating use cases, present talks at conferences, and publish papers in journals. From there we created an exclusive early access program involving a select group of key opinion leaders strategically chosen based on a combination of regional location (so they could be "local" references for our sales force) and application expertise (so they could spread the good word in various important market niches). Their presentations, papers, and references were instrumental in reducing barriers to adoption and driving growth.

Europe was more challenging due to the physical distances we had to travel to visit KOLs, as well as time zone differences and our lack of knowledge of key customers in any given territory. Greg did an admirable job cobbling together a network of sales representatives in certain territories and partner distribution companies in others. Among these, the most important one turned out to be the least expected, and that was in a large territory, Germany. We had already been approached by a German company hoping to sell our products, but the meeting had not gone well. We just hadn't felt comfortable with the company leadership and decided to continue looking.

Around this time I had been invited to speak at a symposium in Basel. Our Swiss distributor, Paul Bucher, had sold Perkin-Elmer products for many years. We knew Paul well, and he had long-term, high-quality relationships with the heads of research and development at all the Swiss pharmaceutical companies. This was a major territory, even if small geographically. Decisions made in Switzerland influenced decisions made at subsidiary companies around the world. Shortly before the meeting I received an email from Michael Weichselgartner, who claimed to represent a major German biotech research products company. Michael wanted to meet me in Basel to talk about a possible business relationship. I was booked so I declined the meeting and instead referred him to Greg.

Michael might have been insulted or incredulous or felt snubbed, but—ignorant of the key players in the German market—I had no idea who he was. As I'd later learn, Michael's company MWG (the company name being Michael's initials) was one of the fastest growing in Germany and had already completed a public offering that valued the company at over a billion dollars. The IPO also left them flush with cash.

Michael pestered Greg to convince him to change my mind, but I was overwhelmed and kept refusing. Greg and I arrived at the conference in Basel, and while watching a speaker talk, I felt a tap on my shoulder and turned around. A distinguished man in a gray suit stood before me, and with a big smile, he stuck out his hand to shake mine and said

"Hello, Dr. Rose, I am Michael Weichselgartner. I drove here just to speak with you. Surely we can find fifteen minutes?"

I was stunned, and preoccupied with the talk I was about to give. I shook his hand and replied, "Michael, what a pleasure to meet you. Unfortunately my talk starts in about five minutes. But this is Greg McGuinness. Why don't the two of you talk, and Greg and I will connect later in the day."

My talk went well, as the crowd was excited to hear the story of our novel pin and ring array making technology, and even more impressed with our "flying objective" laser scanning array imaging system. An hour or so later I bumped into Greg in the hallway, and he said to me "Stan, we need to talk." We walked around until we found an empty conference room.

"So how did your conversation go with Michael?" I asked.

"You won't believe this," he replied. "I told Michael that you meant no insult but are just extremely busy, and that demand for our products is through the roof. I said if he wanted to have any chance to represent us in Germany then he needed to make a bold proposal. Nothing less than a firm commitment to buy fifty instruments this year would do. And he agreed! He'll be placing an order for fifty units just as soon as we can get the distribution agreement in his hands." I never saw it coming, but the relationship with MWG turned out to be the anchor we needed in terms of both volume and credibility in Europe. Greg had played it perfectly, and over time Michael and I would become great friends.

Greg and I continued to travel the world, with him setting up the relationships and me coming in to give seminars to salespeople or to meet key customers. We signed up experienced distributors in the UK, France, Italy, the Benelux region, and the Nordic territories. We flew to Japan to help Takara with their efforts and did a two-day, seven-site blitz in Singapore. Eventually we hit our audacious target of three hundred units sold for the year. It was quite an accomplishment, and even though it was "planned," I'd be lying if I said I knew in advance that we could achieve it.

BARRIER OR OPPORTUNITY?

During my career I've developed a strong understanding of, and respect for, the importance of intellectual property and the limits of the IP protection one can obtain. At the same time, I've always felt that few things truly need to be kept secret. What's important is understanding what those few things are, those most valuable secrets, and having a plan to effectively compete if and when those secrets become known or when their legal protections expire.

By the time we had founded Genetic MicroSystems, a formidable portfolio of issued patents related to the manufacture and use of DNA microarrays already existed. This was one of the reasons I'd been forbidden from pursuing an array scanning system as an employee of Perkin-Elmer or Applied Biosystems. I'm now grateful for that decision, as I may never have started my own company if I'd been allowed to proceed.

A saying from the early days of biotech was that for any given start-up company, you hadn't really made it in your target market until a competitor sued you. Companies rarely bothered suing early-stage ventures that represented no real threat. This was the case with Genetic MicroSystems in our early days too.

We started to garner attention after a conference sponsored by the journal *Nature* and held at the Tanque Verde Ranch in Tucson, Arizona, in 1998. Our poster presentation there discussed a novel method for manufacturing DNA arrays. We described the various patented methods we were not using and showed data demonstrating the high quality of our arrays. We did not, however, disclose how we were making our arrays. It was a big tease and created quite a buzz.

Rob Lipshutz of Affymetrix stopped by during a breakout session to review the poster. After a few minutes of intent reading, he said, "That's really nice work. Have you taken a close look at all our patents?"

"Thanks, Rob," I said. "No, we haven't. But thanks for the heads-up." I had no intention of reading their patents. I preferred to be innocently ignorant for the time being and assumed that Coco had read them closely.

A few months later, at the annual meeting of the American Society of Human Genetics, we had a similar interaction with Greg Yap from Affymetrix. Our own patent applications had been filed by then, and we were openly talking about the pin and ring approach we had developed. We had also begun discussing new methods for imaging DNA microarrays. After I returned to Boston, a large book box with Greg Yap's name on it arrived at the office. Inside I found a stack of patents and patent applications. No threatening letter, however. This was more of a soft warning: if we continued down this path, we were likely to be sued, and that wouldn't be good for our business.

We discussed the Affymetrix IP situation at the next meeting of our board, which now included me, Coco, Pete Honkanen (our VP of engineering), Bob Johnson (director representing angel investors), and Mike Lytton (outside counsel, then with Palmer & Dodge). We knew we couldn't stall forever, and Mike Lytton came up with a creative idea. The scanning system we were developing was much less expensive than Affymetrix's and offered higher-resolution images. Perhaps Affymetrix would want to buy our system and resell it under their label?

The current Affymetrix scanning system was manufactured for them by Hewlett Packard (HP), which was in the process of creating a new life-science-focused spin-off business called Agilent, and that business could be a long-term threat to Affymetrix. What's more, with a list price of $125,000 per unit, we were guessing that HP was selling to Affymetrix at a transfer price of around $75,000 per unit. Our systems could be manufactured for less than $10,000. With this knowledge, Mike suggested that I reach out to Steve Fodor, Affymetrix founder and chairman and someone I had known personally for years. The response from Fodor was quick and clear. They were very interested and wanted to visit us.

The next week a small group visited, led by Rich Rava, Affymetrix's chief technology officer. We had an open and collegial discussion that was highly technical in nature, which is uncommon for a first meeting. We showed them our spotting and scanning systems, prototypes at various stages, software for the user interface, and a manufacturing operation already well underway. The operation had been created from scratch in a few months by Mike Ryan, and our manufacturing capability wound up becoming a key differentiator for GMS. Rich Rava told us that he was impressed with our unique technological ideas and the product performance, but what really encouraged him was our approach to manufacturing, which was light-years ahead of other early-stage companies he had visited. He could imagine Genetic MicroSystems being the seed from which an entire instrument development and manufacturing division could grow.

A larger contingent from Affymetrix visited a few weeks later. Rich came again, but this time the group was led by Sue Siegel, president of Affymetrix. We performed essentially the same dog and pony show for the expanded group, and afterward Sue shared a brief presentation. She nicely summarized her thoughts about the opportunities that Affymetrix was addressing, the size and growth of the target markets, and her vision for maintaining their position as the leading supplier of DNA microarrays.

An unstructured discussion followed. Sue complimented us on all that she saw and then said something to the effect of "I realize that you originally contacted us about reselling your scanners, and you probably have solid plans for growing your business, but would you be insulted if we made an offer to buy your business?"

Neither Coco nor I ever saw that coming. So focused on our own mission, we had never thought about an exit strategy. Or at least we hadn't discussed it explicitly, and in any case, we were only two years into the business. We were just ramping up initial sales, and our primary concern was growth and building out our own unique space in the market.

"No, we're not insulted," Coco said. "We're flattered. Give us a day or two to talk about it."

XXX

AFFYMETRIX ACQUISITION

It didn't take long for us to confer as a board and agree that an acquisition could be ideal—depending on the valuation they had in mind, of course. I relayed the message to Sue, and we agreed to allow them to conduct additional due diligence while we began negotiating a term sheet. Peter Lewis and I were tasked to negotiate the terms of such a deal with Ed Hurwitz, chief financial officer at Affymetrix, and Greg Yap, from the Affymetrix business development team. We had decided that Coco and Sue would stay out of the negotiation, as the process would likely get tense and nobody wanted to risk damaging our long-term relationship at the top level.

Pete and I prepared all sorts of data to justify that Genetic MicroSystems was worth around $150 million. We looked at comparable deals for which data was publicly available. We calculated the discounted net present value of our projected revenue stream. We considered the time and cost that went into developing our technology and associated IP position and what it would take for Affymetrix to replicate that from scratch. Ed and Greg had models of their own, and they came up with a number closer to $30 million. A huge gap.

This was all happening during the second half of 1999, in the midst of the dot-com bubble, when the value of internet and biotech stocks were growing at an incredible rate. The day in May when Affymetrix began speaking with us about acquisition, for instance, their stock was trading at around thirty-five dollars per share. Only a few months later, while we were still debating valuation, the share price had doubled to seventy dollars.

The negotiation had hit an impasse, so one day in July we tried to resolve our differences over a conference call. We each laid out our rationale, anchoring high and low, and made little progress. Coco eventually said, "Why don't we simply agree to split the difference and get this deal done at $70 million? One million shares of Affymetrix stock, currently trading at seventy dollars a share, in exchange for all of GMS stock."

We hadn't discussed this previously, so I asked if we could all please have a moment to talk among ourselves. I thought I had hit the mute button on the speakerphone as I looked at Coco and said, "Are you out of your fucking mind?!" Then, over the speaker, we all heard a voice say, "Guys. You might want to hit the mute button." I was embarrassed, but the message conveyed our team's concern that Coco was making too big a concession here. Even though my mistake was unintentional, it probably helped us in the negotiation.

During the break Coco explained his reasoning. Regardless of what our models said, at $70 million our investors would make a nearly tenfold return after only two years. In addition, as part of Affymetrix, we'd have the re-sources to drive adoption and new product development even faster. If the market kept rising, our stock might be worth even more too. We eventually agreed with his posi-tion, albeit grudgingly for some of us.

When the call resumed, Coco informed the Affymetrix team that we were willing to drop our demand from $150 million to $70 million, provided we agreed on the exchange rate today, with no "collar." To be clear, we wanted to agree on how many shares of Affymetrix stock would be ex-changed for 100 percent of the shares of GMS, and with no high or low point in Affymetrix stock value beyond which we'd go back and reevaluate the exchange rate. No collar. We told them we understood the market was highly volatile, but we wanted to be partners and were willing to take the risk of the stock rising or falling. For better or worse, we would be in this together, for a million shares of Affymetrix stock. Some would consider this a risky move.

Having agreed in July to the key points underlying the acquisition, we still had to complete the legal documen-tation. We moved on to sign a definitive term sheet in September and then wrote up contracts and closed the deal over a few stressful months. This involved preparing and reviewing complex, lengthy documents packed with legal boilerplate and critical aspects of the deal.

The deal was a relatively simple "stock swap." Without a collar, the rest of the deal terms were not complicated. Nonetheless, as with any contract of this type, several areas demanded attention and fine-tuning of the language to be sure that the final documents reflected a deal we could ul-timately sign off on. These typically include the following:

- The definitions need to accurately describe revenue, net revenue, performance milestones, and any setoffs or fees that might reduce the total compensation received.
- The financial terms need to be written in a way that correctly captures the exchange rate agreed to.
- Representations and warranties are the items that the board and key management are asserting to be true. If it were subsequently discovered that some of these were not true, then that could provide an opportunity for the buyer to walk away from the deal.
- Key employee retention plans and/or management carve-outs need to be written with special attention to triggers, notice periods, and definitions of cause and good reason, both in relation to termination of employees by either the company or the employee.

Predictably, we ran into issues never discussed or thought about previously, or where one party or their lawyers didn't agree. Significant negotiation continued while we kept our eyes on the daily operation of our business. Any surprises, in particular "material adverse events," would have put the business's future at risk and given the buyer a reason to void the contract—a worse outcome than simply having the deal fall apart. Those last few months before closing the deal were extraordinarily difficult and stressful. As Yogi Berra famously said, "It ain't over till it's over," and it's over when the deal is actually closed.

As the year was coming to an end, I was immersed in closing the deal while also trying to achieve our year-end target of three hundred units sold. At the same time, I had a long-planned and desperately needed vacation scheduled for mid-December 1999. Elise and I had reserved Limeberry House, a hillside villa overlooking Tortola's Long Bay in the British Virgin Islands, and we were determined to go. As much as I needed a mental break and wanted to check out, my responsibility to my partners, employees, and shareholders required my continued involvement in the Affymetrix deal.

Fortunately the villa had a phone and a fax machine, so we did our best to plan activities that would allow us to enjoy this paradise while also permitting me to check in as needed to review documents. The fax machine was the old type that printed out scrolls. I once found myself sitting on a float in the pool, reading through soaking-wet fax scrolls while quenching my thirst with a sweet mix of local Pusser's Rum and Coke. During the more stressful times I'd be sitting against a wall in the shade, reading through scrolls, and jotting down notes to fax back to the lawyers in Boston.

At last we reached the crossing-of-the-t's-and-the-dotting-of-the-i's part of the negotiation and were ready to formally close. We set a date in February, allowing for Christmas, New Year's, and early January vacations, and the business and reporting activities required of Affymetrix as a public company after every year end.

The deal essentially done, I lay in bed on the second floor of Limeberry House, looking through the open-air screened-in wall and out to a spectacular view over Long Bay to the north. A strong early morning rain pattered the corrugated tin roof, and I wondered if this was all some strange dream. Was I really about to close on my first big deal as an entrepreneur? What an amazing feeling! This lifestyle had me hooked.

In the time since we had agreed on the exchange rate in July, signed the term sheet and announced the deal in September, and eventually closed in February, the price of Affymetrix stock had continued to grow. The September morning we signed the term sheet and announced our deal, Affymetrix stock was already up from $70 per share to $100, and by the end of the day it had closed at $120. Over the next few months, driven primarily by the dot-com bubble, the stock market skyrocketed. By the time we closed in February 2000, Affymetrix stock was trading at $280 per share, and Coco was being hailed as a financial genius.

Affymetrix stock would go on to peak at $324 per share before the market came crashing down. One of our smallest investors, a service provider who liked the company and had invested $25,000, sold his shares at the peak, clearing over $250,000. He put two children through college on his gains from GMS. We were all thrilled!

During the months leading up to the close, we all had to give serious thought as to what our roles would be in this new organization. Coco was given the title of VP of advanced technologies, and he created a team focused on improving the instruments used by Affymetrix or their customers and exploring entirely new ideas. It was the perfect playground for him. I, on the other hand, had no interest in taking on the role of site manager for a remote instrument development and manufacturing operation. Affymetrix president Sue Siegel knew this and offered me the opportunity to move to California and join the company's senior management team as VP of new business development, with a mission to look for new applications and opportunities.

Affymetrix took care of virtually everyone in terms of future roles, responsibilities, and compensation. Almost all realized substantial gains from their stock sales. Senior team members and the board, considered affiliates with confidential information regarding the deal, were required to hold their stock for 180 days. That period was stressful for some, as the market had begun to fall apart. I can't say I wasn't disappointed, but the numbers always seemed surreal to me anyway, and I couldn't do anything about it in any case. I had fun fantasizing about what might have been, but I was satisfied with what came to pass.

Given how hard we had pushed and how far we had come in just a few years, we all felt a need to celebrate. Coco and Kyra hosted a dinner event for the whole company at the Boston Museum of Transportation. Some dressed fancy, others came in costume, and the food and drink overflowed for all. Subsequently I arranged a "strategic planning meeting" in New Orleans for our senior team only. We rented a bunch of rooms in a classy French Quarter hotel and let loose for a few days and nights of "planning," drinking, jazz and blues, and fine Cajun cuisine. When we came home, we all began to consider the next chapters in our lives and wonder what surprises might come our way.

7

NEW PERSPECTIVES

FINDING PARADISE IN ST. JOHN

After recovering from the celebration, we all got back to making, selling, and supporting our instrument systems. In parallel we began the Affymetrix integration, including everything from new employee contracts, benefit packages, reporting relationships, product labeling, promotional programs, and research projects. I began to unload certain Genetic MicroSystems operational responsibilities and started learning about the broader strategic plans for growth at Affymetrix and how I might assist.

Elise and I were excited by the prospect of moving back to the Bay Area and house hunted between September 1999 and March 2000. Real estate prices in California, which had already been high when we left in 1996, had skyrocketed. We would clear enough on the acquisition to afford a nice home in Palo Alto, but we were not comfortable with the extravagant valuations. Paying inflated prices for a small cottage on a postage-stamp-size lot squeezed in between neighbors just didn't feel right. It wasn't only about the money. We just didn't want to live that way. We found some interesting homes near the coast, but a two-hour commute was out of the question.

Depressed with the whole situation, Elise and I decided to rent a small villa on St. John in the US Virgin Islands and spend a week decompressing there in April 2000. We had been visiting St. John regularly for fifteen years, and it had become our favorite getaway spot. We loved to travel and see new places, but every year or so we made sure to find a week to spend on St. John and experience the unique beauty of the place, its people, and its culture.

As luck would have it, on our first day, the forecast called for rain. Sun worshipping would have to wait. Instead we decided to drive into Cruz Bay and explore the island's main town. As we wandered through shops, restaurants, and bars near the ferry dock, we passed American Paradise Real Estate. We stopped briefly to look at the house listings posted on the board outside, and Elise turned to me. "Hey, let's go look at a few houses!"

"What for?" I said. "We've been looking for months in California."

"Just for fun. Let's see how they compare with what we've been seeing in the Bay Area."

I was game. It sounded intriguing. An hour later the whole tone of the day changed. We drove through two stone gateposts and up the long, winding driveway of an estate originally named Featherstone Plantation. Atop the pink-bougainvillea-lined driveway, a stone house built in traditional sugar-mill style sat on the ridgetop, with captivating

water views to the east, south, and west. Sited on a flat par-
cel well over two acres, the home had a nearly constant and
natural form of air-conditioning due to trade winds that
blew in from the east. By the time we finished the tour, Elise
was convinced she'd found her dream home—and she really
wanted it.

There were two problems. First, I was taken completely
by surprise. I had never seriously considered buying anything here. We were house hunting in California! This was
just an outing for fun!

Second, the owner did not really want to sell. The house,
owned by Charlie and Lois Beckwith, was one of the first
homes built in Estate Chocolate Hole on St. John's south
shore. Charlie's health was going downhill, we learned, and
he wanted to move back to the mainland. Lois couldn't bear
to leave. Multiple buyers had made offers, none of them
attractive to Lois. What's more, a week before we visited,
Charlie had increased his list price by $200,000. Elise was
not deterred.

We returned to our rental villa and spent the rest of the
week discussing, debating, agonizing over what to do. Elise
had her mind made up. She wanted this house. I was torn.
How could I possibly make this work? Was it too much to
buy houses on St. John and in California at the same time?
In which house would we live? If St. John, could I really continue to work for Affymetrix? If I left Affymetrix, would
that be a career-ending move?

Eventually I made a decision—several days after Elise
had decided for us both. I reasoned that the market here
was low, still depressed after the damage done by Hurricane
Marilyn in 1995, and that this unique property would

always have value. If anything, the home was at its lowest value now and would likely rise significantly. Purely from an investment perspective, it would be a wise move. More importantly, it would make Elise happy.

I asked our real estate agent to call Charlie and offer him 100 percent of his list price—from two weeks ago, before he raised it by $200,000. She was skeptical he would accept this, but a few hours later I received an excited call: "He's accepted your offer! It must be fate! Lois is finally ready to leave."

We closed on our sixteenth wedding anniversary, May 4, 2000. A fitting date for such an unexpected event. Elise moved in immediately, began making new friends, and quickly immersed herself in the local community. She became vice president of the Animal Care Center, a local nonprofit devoted to caring for the island's stray animals and finding families to adopt them. She never looked back.

I spent the first six months continuing to work for Affymetrix, but with a very long commute. Since St. John doesn't have an airport, I'd have to get a ride to the ferry dock in Cruz Bay, take the boat over to Red Hook on St. Thomas, and travel by taxi between Red Hook and the airport in Charlotte Amalie. During the course of a typical weeklong trip, I would fly St. Thomas to Boston, Boston to San Jose, and San Jose to St. Thomas. At least I tried. Many times I could get only as far as Miami or San Juan on the return trip and had to find a room until the next morning.

After half a year of accumulating frequent-flier miles and spending far too much time away from home, I decided enough was enough. I called Sue Siegel and informed her that I needed to take a formal leave of absence for six to twelve months and then reassess. She understood—in fact, she told me she was jealous, as she had grown up nearby in Puerto Rico and knew just how wonderful this part of the world was. Again, totally unexpected, but I was so fortunate someone like Sue was my superior at this time in my life.

Once I was living on St. John full time, I fell head over heels in love with island life. The Virgin Islands became an integral part of who I was, how I spoke, how I dressed, how I acted toward others, and how I viewed the world. As other St. Johnians (pronounced "Joe-nian") have commented, once you come to live in this place you become a part of it, and it becomes a part of you. That's not to say that a newcomer can adopt or even fully appreciate the same experience as a native multigenerational Virgin Islander. Nonetheless, the place affects your soul.

My next challenge: figuring out how to work remotely from St. John. While many have rethought the traditional office work model since the COVID-19 pandemic took hold in early 2020, this was not common twenty years earlier. Aside from arranging for myself an unconventional setup, I was facing the further challenges of poor cell phone service, internet access via 56K dial-up connections, unreliable telephones, regular power outages due to a teetering local grid, and limited travel options.

Receiving or sending physical materials was an adventure. FedEx did not serve St. John. You had to either go to the airport on St. Thomas or make special arrangements with a taxi service to get a package to the ferry, and then be at the dock to pick it up on arrival. The only courier service that came to St. John was DHL, and there was no home delivery or pickup. DHL delivered once a day (on a good day) to an "office" in a small, weather-beaten shack located down an unmarked, overgrown path in the woods.

High-speed internet access wasn't available until 2003 when a T1 line was put in place from St. Thomas to St. John. At first, connections were limited to a few office suites at Mongoose Junction, a shopping and restaurant plaza in Cruz Bay. I rented an "office" there that was a room the size of a closet, with a simple wooden chair and table, an old rotary telephone, and an Ethernet jack. I'd go there for a few hours a day before or after stopping in at Sun Dog Cafe for lunch.

It took a year or two to settle in, get comfortable with the logistics, and develop an effective way of working remotely. I know it worked well, because not only did I feel good about it, but my shareholders and customers regularly let me know how pleased they were with our relationship and the results. Multiple successful outcomes with different business ventures further indicated that this approach was working.

Despite enduring some hardships and having to adapt to an entirely new way of working, I feel incredibly fortunate to have been able to work remotely from St. John. Having said this, I wouldn't suggest that it's for everyone. Just as with fashion, religion, and politics, one size does not fit all. Working remotely is impossible for many jobs, and even if you're in the right job, it still requires a certain kind of person, especially when you're leading a team.

Some of the keys to success in a remote leadership position are the same as those required to make any start-up work: a solid plan with clearly defined personal objectives; a strong network of established relationships; a senior management team in which you have confidence, who respect your judgment, and with whom you have good, frequent communication; a comfort with handling the logistics around your ability to maintain lines of communication; and a willingness to travel as needed to make it work.

Remote work takes self-discipline and self-motivation and the ability to multitask, mentally compartmentalize, and focus on the tasks at hand. It takes persistence in everything, a tolerance for minor annoyances and major aggravations, calmness under pressure, an ability to navigate past unexpected events, and a commitment to make the process enjoyable for oneself and the rest of the team.

My own experience doing things differently—and learning from others who did things their way too—contributed to a work philosophy I've shared with employees ever since. As long as we embrace a common vision, have respect for one another, understand our individual responsibilities, and accomplish our shared goals, I don't care about when or where you get your work done, how you choose to dress, or any other aspect of your personal life. Different people work at their best in different environments, or they have constraints that require us to be more flexible to access their unique talents.

My biggest fear had been that this move would be career ending, but that fear turned out to be unfounded. Word about my move to St. John and my skill at remote leadership spread through the genomics industry. Everyone wanted to work with me. I would fly north for a day or two, show up at meetings wearing jeans, a Tommy Bahama shirt, and Top-Siders with no socks, and everyone loved it. My new island persona seemed to reinforce my reputation for negotiating good deals and helped me immensely in future fundraising and negotiations. Living on St. John was one of the best experiences of my life, and even if it had ended my career, it would have been worth it.

A NEW MINDSET

One of the biggest challenges I faced on St. John was my lifelong fear of deep water. I had visions of sharks eating me, or of running out of energy and drowning. I drew the line at swimming pools, or in a river or lake where my feet touched the bottom or I felt I could comfortably make it to shore. I'd stay in shallow water when at the beach, and snorkel over reefs provided I could stop and stand up every now and then. At heart I was still a city kid and was most comfortable with my feet on the ground, playing football, baseball, or basketball.

Loren Nickbarg and I met not long after we closed on the house, his wife, Mary, having been our real estate agent. Loren was a charter fishing captain who quickly became my closest friend on St. John. Not only did Loren captain his own boat, but he also ran every aspect of his charter fishing business—with Mary's assistance. He had built up an impressive clientele and was solidly booked all year long. Loren seemed to know *everyone* on the island, in particular the local St. Johnians whose families went back generations.

He was cheerful, fit, and energetic, and frequently flirted in jest with the West Indian ladies who appreciated the fresh fish he sold to them at prices dramatically below what tour-ists would pay in the grocery stores. Loren was known to the locals as "Fisher-mon," and I was immediately accepted simply by association.

On a typical day Loren might bring in yellowfin tuna, mahi-mahi, wahoo, kingfish, or rainbow runners. Oh, and he'd run into plenty of sharks! Not a natural water person, I had no interest in heading twenty miles offshore in a small boat to go fishing with him.

One summer morning, on the tail end of a windy trop-ical wave, Loren drove up my driveway in his beat-up old red Toyota pickup. I was sitting on the veranda, peacefully sipping my morning coffee.

"Hey, Lorenzo! What's up?" I greeted him. "You going fishing this morning?"

"No, not this morning," he said, "but I've got a charter scheduled for this afternoon and was going to go test the water. I wondered if you wanted to come along for the ride."

I thought for a moment and took another sip of coffee. "What does 'testing the water' involve?"

"We'll just run around up the north shore a bit and see if the wind is still blowing, if the surf is still up or not. It's no big deal at all. We won't be going very far out."

I took another sip of coffee and stood up. "Sure, that sounds great. Let me tell Elise I'm heading out for a bit and we can go."

We jumped in Loren's pickup, made the short drive down the hill to a small boater-parking area on Great Cruz Bay, waded out into the shallow water, and got into Loren's wooden dinghy. He didn't bother with a motor but simply rowed out to the mooring where his thirty-three-foot center console boat *World Class* sat. After tying off the dinghy, we slowly putted out past the other boats in the harbor, eventually making our way to the channel on the eastern side, where we accelerated a bit.

We exited the bay and turned starboard toward Cruz Bay and the north shore. Once exposed to the northerly winds and a strong current, the water got choppier. I held on to a stainless-steel pole next to the center console as the boat pounded the oncoming waves with a regular thud, thud, thud. Water sprayed up over the bow each time we smashed into an oncoming breaker, completely soaking us in the exposed cockpit.

As we passed Caneel Bay the sky turned darker, the drizzle intensified into rain, and I started getting concerned. Over the roar of the engine and howl of the wind, I yelled, "Hey, Loren! Is it always like this over here?"

He turned to me with a grin on his face. "Hell no! I'd never take someone out fishing in weather this bad!" Then he started laughing. Images of Captain Dan and Forrest Gump heading into a hurricane flashed through my mind. I held on for dear life but quickly realized the only option was to see this adventure through to the end and have faith in my captain.

Loren turned the boat around shortly thereafter and headed back to the south shore, which was protected from the day's weather. We eventually made it back into Great Cruz Bay, onto the mooring, and into the dinghy for the slow row back to the beach. Once up at the house we had a few midmorning beverages and traded stories. I was slightly pissed at Loren, but more relieved and even a bit thrilled at what he had put me through. I'd taken an important step toward confronting my fears and getting comfortable with a world in which unexpected things can happen and you don't have a choice about it.

While I was on a business trip in California a few months later, Elise called, excited. She had bought a boat. "You did what?!" I thought to myself with a combined sense of surprise and concern. I don't know anything about boats. What kind of boat is it? How expensive? Who's going to teach us how to use it? Where will it be kept? A million questions ran through my head, but I just said "That's great" as I feigned enthusiasm. I had a few more days to ponder the situation before returning home.

It wasn't an expensive boat as boats go. It was a 1985 Beneteau First 29, which was the longest sailboat they made that still had a handheld rudder, and it was stocked with every accessory imaginable. Though I wasn't thrilled at first, I figured I'd just roll with it. Who knows, I might actually enjoy sailing. She was named *Recherche*, which means "research" in French, as well as "rare, exotic, or obscure." It seemed like a good sign to us.

Within a few months, with the help of many local friends thrilled to have an excuse to spend a day on the water, Elise and I learned to care for and sail the boat. We became sufficiently comfortable taking her out on our own and heading down the south shore, or sometimes we'd sail northward and moor at one of the national park beaches. We'd even cross the Sir Francis Drake Channel and drop anchor in White Bay or Great Harbor on Jost Van Dyke in the British Virgin Islands. We kept the boat moored in Chocolate Hole, just down the hill from our house, which we accessed with a dinghy we had tied up on the beach.

In a small community such as St. John, with approximately four thousand year-round residents, most people know one another. This was especially true for those who also had boats moored in Chocolate Hole, one of whom surprised me early one summer morning with a call.

It was not yet 6:00 a.m. but already light out. It was also pouring rain, with the wind blowing and the sky filled with gray-and-black clouds. I picked up the phone.

"Stan, this is Henry Mongie calling. So sorry to bother you at this hour, but you have a dinghy in Chocolate Hole, right?"

"Yes," I replied, barely awake.

"Okay, well, you need to get down there. Meet me there in five minutes."

"Henry, there's an awful storm blowing out there. What's going on?!"

"We have no time to lose! *Impala* has come off her mooring and is headed to St. Croix!"

I was still a bit groggy and trying to take all this in, but I knew that *Impala* was Henry's sailboat.

"Uh, okay, Henry. Give me a few minutes. I'll see you down there."

I jumped out of bed and threw on some shorts, flip-flops, and a long-sleeved T-shirt.

"What's going on?" Elise asked. "Where are you going?"

"That was Henry Mongie. *Impala* came off the mooring and he wants to use our dinghy. I'm going down there to start it up for him. I'll be back shortly." With that I headed out into the rain. The dogs had no interest in following me. They knew better than to head out into a rainstorm. A little river was flowing down our driveway as I drove my Jeep to the beach.

Henry was standing in the rain, waiting for me. "Do you see her faintly out there in the distance?" He pointed to the south.

After straining a bit I could see a boat bobbing way out beyond the head of the harbor. I had no idea how far it was, but the rain was driving sideways and we were both soaked.

"Come on. Let's go," said Henry.

"What do you mean 'Let's go'?"

"I can't go alone. You need to drive the dinghy while I grab the boat."

"Well, shouldn't we call someone and tell them what we're doing?"

"There's no time, Stan. She'll be lost at sea if we don't get going *now*."

Henry was born in South Africa. While in college, he and a band of friends, deciding they could no longer live under apartheid, designed and built a boat so they could leave—having never designed, built, or sailed a boat before. They sailed up the western coast of Africa and then turned to cross the Atlantic. Following the old slave-trading route, the refugees first encountered land in Venezuela, and then made their way north up the chain of eastern Caribbean islands.

When they got to St. John, Henry decided he had found paradise and stayed behind to build a house and a new life there. That was forty years prior, around 1960. Henry was a wonderful man to simply sit with, have a drink, and hear stories about what the world was like back in those days.

He had survived situations much more threatening than the one we were looking at, so I decided. "Okay, let's go."

We jumped in the dinghy, and I pulled the cord to start the outboard and throw it into gear. Off we went straight into the driving rain, squinting to see where we were going. As we exited Chocolate Hole, the seas turned rough, with rolling waves at four or five feet. I felt like we were in a washing machine, and I held on tight to the rope line of the dinghy.

As scared as I was, I knew I had to stay focused. My adrenaline kicked in at full force, and I tried to hold on, stay calm, and keep the dinghy moving toward *Impala*. Slowly but surely she started to come into clearer view. I didn't dare turn around to see how far from shore we'd come. We finally came up alongside the boat, both of us bobbing in the rough seas. Henry stood and grabbed on to one of *Impala*'s railings, and when one of the rolling waves lifted the dinghy, he jumped for it and pulled himself aboard. Now I was sitting in this dinghy alone, bouncing around in hundred-foot-deep water, in the midst of a storm. My worst nightmare come true.

"Stan, throw me a line!" Henry yelled.

I tried to grab the line without letting go of the rope I held to for dear life. I finally was able to grab the line, coil up enough length, and throw it to Henry as the sea tossed us around. Henry caught it, tied it to the boat, and motioned to me to come aboard. I moved gingerly, making sure to keep at least one hand holding a rope, and then watched and waited for the dinghy to raise with the waves while *Impala* fell.

"Come on, Stan!"

I just needed to chance it, so with the next set of waves

I let go of my safety rope, grabbed the boat's railing, got my foot up, and pushed off the dinghy. I made it. We both scrambled inside the cabin and out of the rain. Drenched and exhausted, I turned to the captain. "Henry, does the motor work?"

"I don't know," he calmly replied. "I haven't turned it on in months."

Just great. Now we were out at sea in a storm, possibly with no motor. I suppose we could have raised a sail and tried to navigate in, or I could have gotten back in the dinghy and tried to tow us into Chocolate Hole. That's when I first looked back and saw how far we had come. I really hoped I wouldn't have to get back in that dinghy. Henry opened the hatch to the engine compartment and spent maybe ten minutes fiddling around while I waited and tried to stay calm. The rolling waves didn't bother me at all. There was nothing we were going to bump into.

Finally I heard the sound I was hoping for, the engine kicking in. Henry emerged from the compartment, went to the helm, threw her into gear, and turned us back toward Chocolate Hole. In less than an hour we were back at the mooring. We secured the boat and motored the dinghy back to shore. The wind was still blowing hard and the rain pounding, but I was calm, even elated. We had just ventured into a storm to rescue a boat and had made it back to shore safely.

It's hard to describe the sense of satisfaction and the general confidence that experience gave me. Facing my greatest fear directly, and saving Henry's boat, was an experience I'll never forget. It showed me what I was capable of under extreme pressure. Later in my career I often felt as if things were not going well, the clock was ticking, and the future of the business was on the line. We needed to focus our thoughts, think outside the box, take some risk, leverage our relationships, and get the job done. I learned to rely on the same mindset I had when going after that boat.

Rethinking time was another mindset I adopted on St. John. When most people think about vacationing or living in the Caribbean, their first thought is of "island time." This is really a thing, and it's quite pervasive. Everything moves at a slower pace in the islands. If you're focused on getting work done quickly, this mindset can be annoying. Once you accept it, however, and understand that it stems from challenges with logistics, operating in the heat and humidity, and a general sensibility that there are things in life that are more important than work, it actually becomes quite comfortable. You begin to wonder why everyone else is so rushed and stressed all the time.

Every interaction on St. John begins with a greeting of some sort, such as "Good morning," "Good day," or "Good afternoon." It's considered rude to walk up to someone or call someone on the phone and immediately hit them with a request before taking the time to greet them. Engaging in small talk before getting to the point is even more welcome. I've found that treating people with this little amount of kindness and respect—even when "up north"—goes a long way, and frequently throws people off guard in a good way.

Aside from the benefits of slowing down and treating others with kindness, I learned a variety of other important lessons by living on St. John. It enriches one's soul to take the time to appreciate the physical beauty all around you and the amazing diversity of life. It can be refreshing, energizing, and comforting to carve out time to visit with family and friends and participate in the activities that bring you pleasure. It stimulates your mind and your spirit to engage in informal, spontaneous social activities. It expands your horizons and gives you fresh perspectives when you go on adventures, explore the world around you, try new things, and test your boundaries. By incorporating all these things into your life, you come away more open minded, which can be especially beneficial when approaching new challenges or confronting unexpected situations. I realize it's not practical for everyone to live life this way all the time, but I am incredibly grateful I had the opportunity to do so.

LUCK RUNS BOTH WAYS

At some point I came to believe, and to tell others, that I was a naturally lucky guy. Anyone could see I was full of youthful optimism and self-confidence. I wasn't keeping score, but it seemed things tended to work out favorably for me more often than not. But luck runs both ways, and eventually one should expect to see regression to the mean.

In the big lottery of life, I experienced the rare event of having a malignant thyroid tumor at age thirty. Fortunately it had been found and removed. Now, at age forty-six, having recently sold my first company and relocated to a Caribbean paradise, I was about to experience another rare life event.

It was November 2002, and we had been living on St. John for two years. On this particular day I was in Boston following up on a test result that my primary care physician had found a month earlier. He noticed that the creatinine levels in my blood, a marker of kidney function, had been creeping up slowly but steadily over a ten-year period. It wasn't cause for alarm, but he felt we should check a few things just to be careful.

One of the tests was an abdominal ultrasound to image the kidneys. Shirtless but with a johnny covering the upper part of my body, I lay on an examination bed in a dimly lit room while a technician applied a cold jelly to my abdomen and began an ultrasound. I watched the screen as she moved the probe, and occasionally a solid and distinct shape came into focus. "That's your liver," she said at one point. Okay, I was getting the picture. "Let's take a look at your kidneys next." As she moved the probe, I noticed what I can best describe as an image of a cluster of marbles of differing sizes. I immediately knew what I was looking at, even if it was not something I ever expected to see.

Polycystic kidney disease (PKD) is a genetic condition affecting roughly one in one thousand people in the US. The unusual part for me, however, was that I had no family history of this disease. Apparently it had been caused by a spontaneous DNA mutation, and the proportion of people who get PKD this way is closer to one in twenty thousand. Talk about unexpected events.

I knew quite a bit about PKD even if I never had any reason to suspect I might one day be diagnosed with it. By coincidence, during a postdoctoral fellowship, Elise shared a lab bench at Boston Children's Hospital with Peter Harris, who was studying PKD and would go on to clone the gene responsible for the disease. Peter became a widely acknowledged expert in the field, eventually winding up at the Mayo Clinic. Autosomal dominant PKD is caused by a defect in a single gene located on chromosome 16 in the human genome. The study of the PKD gene, in the hope of developing molecular diagnostic tests or revealing information that might lead to an effective therapeutic, also happened to be one of the projects underway at Collaborative Research when I worked there.

Seeing the marbles on the ultrasound screen, and knowing that my creatinine was rising, I immediately assumed I had PKD. The disease progresses at different rates in different people due to a phenomenon known as *variable penetrance*. As the disease progresses there is a steady decline in kidney function, ultimately leading to the need for dialysis or a transplant to stay alive. Half of those affected may go through their entire lives without ever knowing they have PKD or experiencing any health issues related to it. Unfortunately there was no way to know how fast the disease would progress in any given individual other than to watch it over time.

I left the exam room and went back to the waiting area to share the news with Elise, and she was stunned. She turned a shade of green, and for a moment I thought she was going to vomit. She never expected that once again I would be diagnosed with a serious disease caused by a spontaneous mutation, having survived one resulting in thyroid cancer seventeen years earlier.

Elise insisted I get a second opinion and that we do a molecular genetic analysis to confirm what was really going on. The thought that I might one day need a kidney transplant was just too much to handle. I didn't disagree, but I also couldn't get my mind off the image of marbles on that ultrasound screen. Whether or not I had the genetic mutation, my kidney function was slowly declining and the organs were riddled with cysts.

Typical of me in stressful situations where I believe I've done all I can do, I chose to compartmentalize it, to set it aside and not overreact. A band called the Other Ones, the remaining living members of the Grateful Dead, were playing at the Boston Garden. It was the perfect opportunity to take my mind off things, enjoy some live music, and remind myself that I might never have a problem with this disease. Or perhaps an effective drug would be developed by the time I needed it! Always the optimist.

For the next eight years, every three to four months, I would visit Dr. Julian Seifter, a nephrologist at Brigham and Women's Hospital ("the Brigham"). The first successful kidney transplant was performed at the Brigham by Dr. Joseph Murray in 1954. There was arguably no better place to get care for someone who might go on to experience end-stage renal disease.

Dr. Seifter is a kind and soft-spoken man who personally understands what it's like to live with chronic illness. He himself suffered from juvenile diabetes. In 2010 he published *After the Diagnosis*, an insightful, moving, and inspiring book about how people cope and even thrive with chronic disease.

Each visit was the same. I would have my blood drawn and my creatinine measured, and afterward Dr. Seifter and I would talk about how I was feeling and measure my blood pressure (which is regulated in part by hormones made by the kidneys). Then he'd ask me to sit on the exam table so he could feel my cystic kidneys. Rarely was there anything particularly interesting going on, which was good news for me. As another physician friend once told me, "In the field of medicine, you never want to be viewed as interesting."

Toward the end of each visit, Dr. Seifter would ask me if he could have a student or resident come in and feel my cystic kidneys, which I always approved. After all, the Brigham is a Harvard teaching hospital, and I was happy to help young physicians gain useful experience. After an anonymous physician in training massaged my abdomen, Dr. Seifter would send me home with the same message: it was impossible to know if or when things might progress to the point that I'd need to consider dialysis or a transplant, so don't spend my time worrying about it.

8

GENOME STRUCTURE AND FUNCTION

NIMBLEGEN OPPORTUNITY

You can never predict whether an apparently random person you meet will, over time, become a close friend or key business contact. Partly for this reason, and partly out of simple courtesy, I always made a habit of trying to make a good first impression with new contacts and treating people with respect and kindness. Virtually everyone has an interesting story to tell if you're willing to listen, and you never know when some aspect of their experience might become relevant or even critical to your business or your life. Much as a CEO should be constantly fundraising and pitching their company's story, any professional should be constantly building relationships.

After establishing my operating capabilities from St. John, one of my first projects involved assisting Dr. David Schwartz and his scientific collaborators at the University of Wisconsin to found a new company called OpGen and secure initial financing. This required occasional trips to Wisconsin to meet with prospective investors. One such group was led by two brothers, Bob and Tom Palay, whom we first met for dinner on a cold, snowy night in 2001. That dinner meeting did not go well.

We arrived late by a good half hour, trudging into the restaurant with snow-covered parkas, looking far from professional. Sitting at a table were Bob and Tom, in beautifully tailored gray suits, frowns on their faces. Bob and Tom were fascinating people with wry senses of humor and great questions, but the chemistry between the two brothers and the scientific founders was terrible. Worse, after the meeting, David's partners told me they were seeking "a real VC" and didn't understand how helpful these "super angels" could be. My view at the time was that this was going to be *their* company, and I wasn't going to push them to take money from any group they didn't feel comfortable with, no matter the reason.

The Palay brothers may not have clicked with OpGen's scientific founders, but they realized the value I could bring to another business in which they had invested, NimbleGen Systems. I recalled the paper NimbleGen had published in *Nature Biotechnology* in late 1999 while we at GMS were trying to close our deal with Affymetrix. NimbleGen had cleverly invented an alternative way to make Affymetrix-quality high-density DNA microarrays. They used the Texas Instruments digital light processors (a key component of consumer video projectors) to precisely illuminate discrete spots on surfaces and drive photochemical reactions in only those locations. This made it unnecessary to invest in the costly and time-consuming development of physical masks to direct where light-mediated reactions would occur, as Affymetrix had. It also simplified design changes. This was a brilliant idea, and the technology worked! Unfortunately the fledgling business was struggling.

Headquartered in Madison, and with a small chemistry group in Germany, NimbleGen was prevented from making or selling arrays in the US or other major markets by patents owned by others. Instead they manufactured arrays in Iceland, where there were no issued patents affecting them, and operated as a custom service provider. Scientists would pay NimbleGen to produce custom-designed arrays and then send their DNA samples to Iceland, where the company would analyze them using the custom-manufactured arrays. Sending results back to scientists anywhere in the world was no problem as patents couldn't be used to prevent the free flow of information generated legally, but this business model proved challenging to grow rapidly.

When Bob called me a few weeks after the OpGen dinner meeting and asked whether I'd be open to working with NimbleGen, I still had a noncompete agreement in place with Affymetrix that would not expire for another year. I told Bob that I couldn't even talk with them about that business. Polite and professional, he told me he'd give me a call in a year. I'm not sure I believed him and pretty much forgot about it.

Exactly one year later, in the winter of 2002, the phone rang in my home office on St. John. It was Bob Palay again. I told him I was happy to talk now but I wasn't sure how much help I could be with NimbleGen. I was perfectly content with what I was doing on St. John and didn't especially want more responsibility. I was sailing three days a week, and we had a major renovation going on at the house.

I suspected Bob might want to pick my brain a bit, hire me for a short consulting gig, or maybe even try to get me to join NimbleGen's board. He clearly needed help figuring out how to grow his business. What Bob had in mind, however, was something I had never considered. He wanted me to become the company's new CEO.

Bob is one of the most insightful, persistent, and persuasive people I know. He likes to tell people he's just a "hick from Milwaukee," but he graduated from Harvard and obtained his law degree from Northwestern. Before becoming an angel investor and managing his family office with his brother, Tom, Bob had worked for Sam Zell, founder of Equity Group and one of the wealthiest men in the world. If you haven't yet read Sam's book, *Am I Being Too Subtle*, I highly recommend it.

I must confess that I was indeed missing the thrill of the start-up experience that I had lived through at GMS. I was also missing being amid major scientific advances. As I sat on St. John, the US-government-sponsored Human Genome Project and the privately funded company Celera were competing to complete the first human genome sequence. Worldwide, genome researchers were gearing up for a new phase of exploration and viewing the genome sequence not as an end but as a means to create a reference database that could be used to study the enormous complexity of genome variation and regulation. Such a tool would open the door to new discoveries and applications.

I loved living on St. John. I had a lot of angst over the original decision to move there, thinking it could be a career-ending move. As things turned out, it was the best experience of my life, and I was able to continue to keep a finger in the world of biotech while living a near-perfect work-life balance. I had zero interest in going back to work full time, but I was a bit conflicted and Bob saw an opening. Bob said, "How about if you become our CEO at NimbleGen, but you only work part time and you do it from St. John?"

I was stunned. "Well, I never thought about that as a realistic possibility. I have to think about it. On the surface it sounds great, but do you really think it could work? I don't want to get involved in something that's doomed to fail from the start and winds up being a waste of both of our time."

"Don't worry about that," Bob said. "Right now my options are to have you working with us part time and remotely, or someone far less qualified full time and in Madison. It's an easy decision. How about if you speak with some of the other board members and see what they think?"

I agreed, and all those interactions went well until the last one. John Freund was the founder and general manager of Skyline Ventures. He was a triple Harvard graduate (undergrad, MD, MBA), had created the healthcare investment banking practice at Morgan Stanley, and was a super-likable guy. An aggressive New Yorker mellowed and polished a bit by living part time in San Francisco, he moved at a pace that was very comfortable to me. He was fast, to the point, and laser focused on getting important things done. I liked John, which made it all the more difficult when he convinced me that I couldn't do justice to this job remotely and part time, and that's exactly what I told Bob.

Bob did not take this news well and insisted that John

was wrong. "John's being way too cautious. I'll speak with him. He doesn't understand how well this can work. He's just not thinking creatively enough."

"No," I replied, "I think he's actually right. We're fooling ourselves. Being CEO, especially in what is essentially a turnaround situation, is just going to take more effort than I can give right now."

"Stan, you're not going to be in this alone." Bob was insistent. "I'll be there with you every day, helping get you up to speed, managing relationships with the rest of the board, and helping fill in wherever you need it. Also, Tom will be on the ground in Madison every day. He's not only vice chairman; he's also chief operating officer. He'll handle all the day-to-day issues. Trust me, you'll love the rest of the team, and with your inspiration and leadership I know we can make this work. It would be such a great story—nobody would be able to ignore us."

"I don't know, Bob. John made a lot of sense to me."

"Don't think about John. How about this? Why don't we just give it a try and see what happens? If it doesn't work after a few months, we go our separate ways. No harm, no foul. Okay?"

I thought for a few moments. "Okay," I said with some hesitation. "I'm willing to give it a try, as long as we all go into this with our eyes open. We have to agree on key objectives for the first year. I have to know what three to four things are most important. I have to be able to put together a strategy and a story that I honestly believe and am excited about, and can communicate to the rest of the employees as well as any investors or potential partners."

"Absolutely," he said. "Why don't you spend a few days thinking that over, come up with a proposal, and we can talk about it. While you're doing that, I'll circle back with John and the rest of the board and get them to sign on to the plan. Do we have a deal?"

"Sure, Bob. We have a deal. Let's give it a shot!"

Over the next few days I thought a lot about not only objectives for myself and the company, but also my motivations for getting involved in any new business. I finally settled on the following list of key criteria:

- I have to be excited about the science.
- I have to believe I'd enjoy working with the team.
- I have to see an opportunity to create substantial value for all stakeholders in a reasonable period of time.

NimbleGen appeared to fit all these criteria. Later I would add a fourth:

- The business has to have some kind of personal meaning to me, some impact on my own life.

It didn't take long for me to come up with key goals for the coming year. Bob and I reached agreement shortly thereafter. Within a few weeks the rest of the board had signed on. Bob likes to tell people about how he "talked me off the beach." His version of the story is that I was literally on the beach when he called me about the NimbleGen CEO role, in one of the most beautiful spots in the world. He considered me "a star . . . the right guy to lead NimbleGen" and so treated me that way. He listened carefully to what I wanted and needed to join, and made sure I got it. If that meant I wanted to live and work only part time from St. John . . . perfect, they'd make it work. Over time, I found I enjoyed working with the NimbleGen team, and eventually came on full time.

Bob's version is all true, but I also kept my word that I wouldn't move from St. John.

$$\bowtie$$

A STRATEGY FOR GROWTH

Most of my time working as CEO of NimbleGen was spent on St. John, usually from my small home office just off the master bedroom—although I did occasionally take calls from a boat, or a bar stool, or a beach. My home office was a converted walk-in closet, but it did have a mahogany desk and a window from which I could see the blue water of Great Cruz Bay down below us to the west. The dogs loved to come up outside the window, stand on their hind legs with paws on the glass, tilting their heads from side to side trying to figure out what I was doing sitting inside this room on a glorious Virgin Islands afternoon.

I had a telephone and a computer in the office, although in the beginning I had only a 56K dial-up connection for internet access and unreliable phone service (and power!). Nonetheless, I would sit at my desk in bare feet, shorts, and sunglasses, and conduct conference calls over the phone. I used to refer to it as the *"Charlie's Angels* school of management," with me as Charlie and my distant senior management team as my angels.

Shortly after the public announcement of my CEO appointment, I paid a visit to Affymetrix in Santa Clara, California. I had enjoyed working with Affymetrix, and though my noncompete had expired, I had a great relationship with founder Steve Fodor and president Sue Siegel—and I wanted to keep it that way. So I called their joint executive assistant just after signing on with NimbleGen and asked if she could set up an in-person meeting for me as soon as convenient. It's important to know that NimbleGen's board had been shamelessly pitching the company to be sold since the beginning, and Affymetrix was an obvious candidate to acquire the company. This was due in part to Affymetrix's blocking IP position, but also because it would eliminate a potential competitor in the marketplace for high-density DNA arrays. At the same time it would give Affymetrix a solution for addressing the custom-designed array market.

As I walked into Steve Fodor's office—in a building in the same Santa Clara industrial park as Yahoo!—I found him sitting comfortably with his feet up on the desk. With a big grin, Steve said, "Rose, if I didn't know better I'd say you're being pretty opportunistic here." The message was delivered in a friendly voice, with some gentle ribbing. I smiled and said, "C'mon, Steve, you have to admit this was a pretty good fit for me. And it actually could be a great relationship for both of us."

I didn't try to make a sales pitch because that was never my intent. I was just trying to make sure we had open lines of communication. I also wanted to avoid inadvertently insulting Steve or Sue immediately after the termination of my noncompete agreement.

We were always surprised that Affymetrix had never made an attempt to buy NimbleGen, but we did start a conversation that day that led to a different kind of relationship that we had never anticipated. Sue and Steve proposed that we form a partnership under which Affymetrix would sell arrays produced by NimbleGen, custom designed to specs provided by Affymetrix customers, and packaged in proprietary GeneChip cartridges limiting use to only Affymetrix hardware systems. NimbleGen could make these arrays rapidly, and Affymetrix would market the new product line under the brand name NimbleExpress Arrays.

This was the first and only time Affymetrix ever put an array manufactured by another company in a GeneChip cartridge. The product line wound up being meaningful to NimbleGen during the following year but did not have a big impact on the top line at Affymetrix, which probably soured them a bit on the idea of acquisition. Nonetheless, it gave us an opening to move out of the pure service business and sell arrays. Moreover, the arrangement validated our technology in the eyes of customers and competitors, which became important over the next two years.

During my first year at NimbleGen, I spent a lot of time observing, taking notes, and talking to people throughout the organization (from the board to the janitors). I was trying to refine my mental model of the company and develop as thorough as possible an understanding of what was actually going on, who did what, who were the impact players, what was working and what was not, who was happy and motivated, and who was clearly slacking off and a bad influence.

At the same time, I was monitoring competitors' and potential partners' movements in the marketplace and getting up to speed on our financial position. I was determining which board members were most likely to be helpful going forward and which of my industry contacts might be interested in participating in our next round of financing— and which story would best convince them (and myself!) that investment made sense.

There were two critical decisions I had to make, or more precisely two categories of actions to consider. The first involved reconfiguring my senior management team. Several personnel issues became clear to me over that first year. A commercial team barely existed, and that needed to change. Fortunately I had a strong network in this functional area. In short order I recruited several reliable people I had worked with previously. They built a North American sales, customer service, and support organization and an export sales organization from scratch.

Next, I realized that Emile Nuwaysir was being vastly underutilized and deserved to be promoted to the vice president level to lead our business development activities. Emile had been with NimbleGen since the beginning, was well liked by all, and commanded everyone's respect. I trusted his knowledge, judgment, and instincts and immediately clicked with him on a personal level. He quickly became one of my most valuable team members.

Two additional key positions needed addressing. When I arrived at NimbleGen, the Iceland production facility was overseen by an individual in Madison. Over time (and many trips to Iceland), I concluded that the person who understood that operation best was also eminently qualified to lead it, without any intermediary. That was Sigridur Valgeirsdottir ("Sirry"), whom I promoted to vice president and member of the senior team.

Last but not least, with the help of Bob Palay, we were able to attract David Snyder to join us as chief financial officer. Bob had known David from their days working together for Sam Zell. David impressed me immediately, and to this day I can't think of another CFO who speaks so beautifully when talking about financials; makes the implications of numbers so easy for anyone to understand; and can professionally manage an analyst call, an IPO process, or any other strategic financing matter that may come along. With these changes in place, I felt I had the right team on the ground to lead the company forward.

The second big decision was around commercial strategy. From the day the company was founded, everyone thought that NimbleGen's biggest advantage over other platforms was its ability to make custom-designed arrays. I understood how difficult the custom service business could be, however, and while it wasn't impossible to build a growing business based on custom products, it did present a number of challenges (e.g., small batch sizes, especially difficult array designs, and an inability to focus marketing, sales, or support on any single large segment of customers). My epiphany was the realization that the same capability that allowed us to make custom designs also enabled us to rapidly make and test and optimize new designs for emerging applications of genome analysis, each of which could be addressed with a single fixed-design array.

The idea's inspiration came from two sources. First, the seed planted by Coco Montagu at GMS regarding the whole notion of rapid prototyping. Second, the collaboration that our scientists had developed through their involvement in the NIH ENCODE project, which was led by Francis Collins at NIH. I sat through meetings discussing new applications of array-based analysis being developed and used for the ENCODE project. These included testing for genome-wide methylation patterns, copy number variants, and chromatin immunoprecipitation assays on arrays (called *ChIP-chip*, and used to reveal patterns of protein binding to isolated DNA).

One day it dawned on me that each of these applications had the potential to become as big as gene-expression monitoring or analysis of single nucleotide polymorphisms, the main two uses for DNA arrays. The difference was that the markets for these new applications were wide open. We could be the first to market and establish a standard that others would have a challenging time following quickly. Taking advantage of unique opportunities such as this, which you simply can't plan, can make the difference between success and failure. The question remained as to whether or not we'd be able to capitalize on the opportunity.

SCALING THE BUSINESS

By late 2006 we had shifted the business into high gear. With Affymetrix as a partner, a new commercial team, new senior team, new strategy, and an effective marketing campaign, we were rapidly growing. I don't mean to imply that it was all smooth sailing from here on out. Beware the inevitable unexpected events.

As we scaled our production capacity in Iceland, for instance, one day we found that our standard protocols for array analysis no longer worked. We could not produce images to analyze, meaning that our business was dead in the water. With customers anxiously awaiting their data, and our board wondering whether we had built a soon-to-crumble house of cards, our scientists scrambled to troubleshoot the problem. They quickly reasoned that the problem had to be with our chemistry, but it was anybody's guess which component might be at fault.

Through the tireless work of the entire team, a hypothesis came to light. One of the key chemicals used in processing our DNA arrays had for years been delivered to us in very small bottles that were transported to Iceland by air. Now that we were using larger quantities, we had begun purchasing this chemical in barrels, and these were shipped by sea. Our scientists tested the chemical solutions for purity and found small levels of contamination with water. Just enough to interfere with the normal reaction. Apparently, tiny amounts of water had seeped into the containers while crossing the Atlantic. Once that water was evaporated, the reactions began working normally again.

Then there was the problem NimbleGen had faced from day one regarding intellectual property rights. We had secured just enough of a license from Affymetrix to be able to expand our operations from offering services out of Iceland to now producing and shipping arrays directly to customers.

We did not, however, have all the rights we needed to position ourselves as a viable investment in an initial public offering without the liability of a potential lawsuit. The same could be said for any acquisition by another company.

The problem's solution came in a very unexpected and creative manner. One day, near the end of the financial quarter, I received a call from a lawyer at a public company that owned some of the patents to which we needed access. This lawyer, whom I'll refer to as "Jim," had worked with me previously, so we had an established relationship.

"I have a somewhat unusual proposition for you," Jim started in. "We both know that you need licenses to several issued claims we have. As it turns out, you may have something we could use, but we'd need to act quickly." I was intrigued, and I was sure we could move quickly. Our company wasn't called NimbleGen for nothing. Jim continued, "You know that the quarter is coming to an end next week, and we're concerned that we may be off on our revenue target by just a bit. We were wondering if there might be something we could sell you that would cover the difference."

I didn't have to think long about it. "How much do you need, Jim?"

Jim gave me a reasonable number, and I called our board members to discuss. In less than twenty-four hours, we agreed to pay them for a limited license to some of the intellectual property we needed. We repeated this same dance at the end of the next two quarters and in less than a year had secured all the rights we needed to open up multiple paths for financing or exits going forward.

Between the costs of securing freedom to operate and

the added expenses associated with a larger and growing revenue stream, it was clear we needed more funding. The board decided the time was right to raise a large amount through an initial public offering. We invited a group of top investment bankers to meet with us at the Hilton Chicago O'Hare hotel for a "bake-off." Each group would give us their best pitch regarding how they would present our story to investors, what value they thought we could command in the public markets, how much money we could raise, and how their firm's research analysts could help spread the word about us in support of retail sales of our stock.

We chose to work with Chris O'Connor and his team at J.P. Morgan as lead, even though they didn't present the most aggressive proposal in terms of predicted valuation. We just felt comfortable with Chris, and it didn't hurt that the J.P. Morgan Healthcare Conference—held in San Francisco every January—was the biggest event in the life science investment industry. We also agreed to pull three other firms into the syndicate, broadening sales coverage for our stock and, more importantly, giving us additional widely followed industry analysts who would publish research reports on NimbleGen. The high-level plan was to raise enough money to accelerate our growth, stay independent, and drive up our value in the public markets with the help of the analysts, all cheering us on and promoting our stock.

There was a strong argument to be made for the IPO path, but there also was what's known as "execution risk." For longtimers who understood what it took to build a successful company and keep it growing, the fear of inevitable unexpected events remained. The less risky approach might have been to simply cash out today and sell the company to a strategic acquirer for as much money as possible. That amount would likely be lower than what one might imagine we could capture over time as a public company but would provide immediate liquidity for investors and resources to more rapidly grow the business.

The debate raged on internally, and truth be told, I favored the alternative M&A (mergers and acquisitions) path. My public position as CEO, however, had to be "I'm completely confident about our ability to grow this business and committed to going it alone" (which was a true statement). "We're happy to talk with anyone, but we have no plans to sell this business early." Any other position would have indicated weakness, would have given potential buyers pause, and would have negatively affected our valuation in an IPO. So while the rest of the board argued the merits of selling now versus going it alone, I had no choice but to insist that we were planning to go public. I would stick with that message unless a firm made an acquisition offer so attractive I'd be obligated to reconsider.

The next few months proved to be the hardest of my career. Simultaneously, I had to lead parallel team efforts to prepare the company for an IPO and work with our bankers on all its details, negotiate secretly with half a dozen companies interested in acquiring NimbleGen before an IPO, and keep the business growing and hitting our quarterly targets. Failure to achieve or exceed our now publicly known quarterly performance metrics would have been disastrous. All this while commuting from St. John and trying to keep my home life stable.

We were planning to raise $75 million through an IPO

at a premoney valuation of $175 million, for a postmoney valuation of $250 million. Any offer to buy the business pre-IPO had to price us at some premium over $250 million. Our sales were at a monthly run rate equivalent to $20 million a year, so we were seeking a 13x or greater multiple. The industry comparables were all at around 5–6x, so this was fairly aggressive. On the other hand, we had a scarce asset that was of great strategic value to multiple parties. Amid all this, another unexpected event occurred that further supported a higher valuation.

One of our scientists had been working on an innovative idea in which DNA arrays would be used not for analytical purposes but for preparative ones. The arrays would be designed to bind (or capture) specific fragments of DNA that one wanted to sequence, and then be processed so that the bound DNA fragments would be removed into a solution. The resulting solution was thus enriched for the DNA of interest. Instead of having to sequence all the DNA from an original sample, you now had to sequence only a tiny fraction, containing only targeted regions of interest. This enrichment technology (also referred to as *sequence capture*) dramatically reduced the time and cost of performing targeted DNA sequencing. Now we had the attention of every DNA sequencing company, and the M&A track in the dual-track process started to really heat up.

Over the ensuing months we met with most of the biggest companies in the genome analysis space. In-depth due diligence was performed, offers floated, and counters provided, and the field narrowed as our price grew beyond what some were prepared to offer. In the end, there was one group left standing, with a proposal that stood above the rest.

⋈

ROCHE ACQUISITION

Roche had collaborated with NimbleGen in the past, and we had been talking for nearly four years before the current round of discussions. They had always been attracted to our DNA array technology but also had their own horse in the DNA sequencing race. Our sequence capture technology could be the jockey that goaded them to the head of the pack.

Once we signed a term sheet, the slow-moving, aircraft-carrier-size organization transformed into a SWAT team overnight. Nearly fifty people from Roche descended on us in Madison, taking over one of the local hotels. In a matter of days they scoured through every aspect of our business. Their speed and efficiency were shocking at first, but not so surprising when one considered that this was a Swiss organization that had demonstrated success in business for more than a hundred years.

As the proposed closing date approached, I was summoned to a key meeting in Zurich. Roche Applied Science head Manfred Baier had reserved a room at the airport, where we sat across the table from each other and went through a list of our key people. Manfred wanted my feedback on whether their assessment of the value of each of these individuals was correct, and if so, what it would take to retain each of them. My name was at the bottom of the list, and I could see from across the table that it was crossed out.

After a good two hours, we had covered everyone on the

list except for me. Manfred looked up at me. "Well, Stan, we know how much equity you have in this company, and we don't expect that we can make any kind of offer that would entice you to stay on."

I thought for a moment. "I understand why you may think that, but I tried retiring once and I wasn't very good at it. I'm still pretty young, this field is getting more exciting every day, and I'll most likely want to find some way to play a role in it."

That opened up a completely unexpected discussion, which led to me agreeing to stay on for at least a year, in large part to help ensure a smooth transition and a successful investment for Roche. In return, Manfred agreed to a compensation package substantially greater than mine at NimbleGen, and immensely fair.

We held a company meeting in Madison to announce the closing and brought champagne for the occasion. I gave a talk to all our employees, congratulating them on their accomplishments and painting a picture of a future under Roche that could be exciting for all of them—and important to Madison, as this big company was now putting down roots in the upper Midwest. Manfred shared his own vision and his enthusiasm for working with our people in Madison, Iceland, and Germany.

As the meeting ended and people were filing out, somebody said to me, "I thought you said that if we ever closed this deal, we were going to have a big party." That really struck me, as this person was correct. I had gotten so caught up in bringing these two companies together that I hadn't given sufficient thought to appropriately celebrating our success. I went to the airport that afternoon and flew home, the entire trip back spent thinking about throwing a big party in Madison.

Once home, I started googling event venues in Madison, live bands, catering, and such. I narrowed down my list to three theaters in town and emailed each one inquiring about hosting a private party. A few minutes later my phone rang. It was a fellow named Steve who owned the Barrymore Theatre in Madison, a two-thousand-seat venue used mostly for rock and roll concerts. Steve started in: "Well, I see you have a 617 phone number, so you must be a Red Sox fan." He was calling from Madison, but I could hear a hint of a New York accent.

"As a matter of fact," I said, "I was born in the Bronx and have been a lifelong Yankees fan!"

"Me too! We should catch a game together sometime. But meanwhile, I can help you with everything you need for your party."

I had a good feeling about Steve, but just to be sure I called one of my VPs in Madison and asked him if he knew the theater and what he thought of the idea. He knew it well, and assured me this was a good choice. We invited several hundred people, and the event was the talk of the town. Steve had "Congratulations NimbleGen" spelled out on the marquee over the theater entrance on the day of the party. As they say, a fine time was had by all. It was one of those events people talked about for years.

In the afterglow of the Barrymore party, as word spread through the company, I realized I needed to plan something similar in Iceland. I called Sirry, told her what we had done in Madison, and asked for her help planning an Icelandic version. She wound up booking a restaurant/bar in downtown Reykjavik and a local band, and a week or so later I flew there for the party. My dad was now retired and had never been to Iceland, so I invited him along to the party and a few days of sightseeing afterward.

In true Icelandic tradition the evening started slowly but gained momentum. The initial cocktail party with music was followed by dinner, followed by more drinking, dancing, and music, before we eventually stumbled into the street.

It might have been well after midnight, but things were just getting going. The next phase involved an after-party at someone's house, with everyone pitching in by bringing everything from cases of beer to buckets of ice and all the ingredients to mix a potent magic punch. I dropped my dad back at the hotel and then joined my fellow employees at the party. Sometime before dawn I finally left, wandered Reykjavik's cobblestone streets toward the hotel, and crawled into bed.

After a few hours of sleep, Dad and I had a full breakfast and headed out in the car to drive the Golden Circle, a nearly two-hundred-mile route through Iceland's southern uplands. In eight hours we got to see some of the Reykjavik area's more famous sights, including the magnificent waterfalls at Gullfoss, the original geysers at Geysir, and the site where warring tribes came together to form one of the earliest documented democracies at Thingvellir.

On the drive back Dad spotted on our map a road headed toward what we assumed was a small fishing village. We decided to take the detour and wound up driving on gravel for nearly two hours, passing not a single car coming the other way and crossing terrain that looked like the face of

Mars. Once we hit the coast we found only a small crooked roadside sign acknowledging the name of the place, but not a single building. Instead of being disappointed we both just laughed it off. Dad loved the trip and told me it was one of the best vacations he'd ever taken. Moments like that make it all worth it.

The NimbleGen story was jammed full of unexpected events that resulted in a surprisingly positive outcome for all. We had pioneered the concept of remote management for small biotech businesses, shown how well it could work, and demonstrated what was required for success. I learned the importance of never entering a deal that might inadvertently provide access to a company's most valuable assets. In our case, these were our array manufacturing systems, which many had wanted to purchase. As Tom Palay would frequently say, "We won't sell you a single unit, but we'll sell you *all* of our units." I learned, yet again, that there are many creative and legal ways around IP positions, so one should avoid the knee-jerk reaction to pass up an opportunity simply due to perceived IP constraints.

Once again I saw the impact of personal relationships, the power of developing strong ties with partners and employees, and the benefits of thinking creatively about how to enable others to thrive in their jobs. I also learned about something Tom Palay called the "PITA scale," which stood for "pain in the ass." When dealing with difficult people, or those needing extensive support or hand-holding, one had to consider how much that individual contributed versus how difficult they were to work with (or replace).

The most important thing we accomplished was building a healthy, growing business that enabled scientists to study new classes of genome variation—and eventually, to use arrays for targeted sequence enrichment before sequencing. We developed strong relationships with key opinion leaders in the field who evangelized these new capabilities, and we created a business of great strategic value to multiple potential acquirers. By filing to take the company public and having our S-1 registration statement seen by all those interested, we created an auction environment in which J.P. Morgan bankers were able to run a dual-track process that culminated in a great outcome for our shareholders.

I stayed on as president of Roche NimbleGen for nearly eighteen months. Just long enough to ensure that the new management from Roche knew what they were dealing with and that all our employees had a chance to either secure their roles within the merged company or find new positions elsewhere. I regularly traveled to Germany for meetings of Manfred's senior staff, often sharing outlier opinions or speaking up when others feared to.

Manfred and I developed a close relationship, and he especially appreciated my honesty and candor when others prioritized political correctness. He became a great mentor. However, once my day-to-day activities started to get less interesting and more bureaucratic, I knew it was time for me to move on and find the next big thing.

9

INVESTING IN GENOMICS

ROSE VENTURES BLACK SWAN FUND

Following the Roche acquisition, I was still leading the NimbleGen organization, but my role had fundamentally changed. No longer focused on financing, partnering, and gaining IP access, my biggest concern now was overseeing the integration—doing all I could to keep the business growing, prevent Roche's changes in management from steering us down the wrong path, and protect the former NimbleGen employees. I had no idea how long this next stage of my career might last.

Over the ensuing year, a number of long-term Roche employees from their talent pool had been assigned to various vice president roles at NimbleGen. Most of the original NimbleGen employees who wanted to engage in new opportunities had moved on. I used to joke that at times I felt like the captain on a sinking ship, refusing to leave until all my crew were safely ashore.

Having been through acquisitions, it didn't surprise me that the new management had different ideas about business strategy. Of most significance, they wanted to leverage NimbleGen's sequence capture products to help sell Roche's sequencing systems by selling them only as a package. I argued for a different approach. I thought it would make more sense to establish NimbleGen's sequence capture technology as the first choice for use with *any* sequencing system on the market. We were first to market with a compelling new technology and had the opportunity to capture the front end of *all* targeted DNA sequencing. Unfortunately the Roche Applied Science divisional management team consistently outvoted me. Their primary concern was how to sell more sequencing systems.

When the time came, I was transparent about my decision to leave. Because of the strong relationships I had developed with Manfred and Roche's senior management, I was able to continue consulting for Roche and assisting the business when needed. Having lived the PCR business experience and sold two companies that similarly provided high-impact tools, I wanted to find a new opportunity to yet again achieve the same kind of emotional highs and commensurate financial rewards. I wasn't sure at all what form it would take, but I knew I'd need some kind of a legal entity and administrative support. I reached out to the former NimbleGen lawyers at Godfrey & Kahn in Madison for assistance, and we created an entity called Rose Ventures Inc. (RVI).

The name was chosen playfully, with no idea whether we'd ever be in the venture capital business. Rather, it was intended to convey the fact that this company would pursue whatever ventures interested the principal. Those might include consulting, advising, directing, or investing. I created a budget plan for the year and thought about it as an investment. Courtney Schieve, a University of Wisconsin genetics grad and former NimbleGen employee, came to work with me as executive associate. I had gotten to know Courtney through visits during my open office hours and came to find her a smart, quick, driven person who was an independent thinker, cared about the quality of her work, and had a degree of enthusiasm and commitment that resonated with me.

Courtney was eager to learn about the world of business and unafraid to give me honest opinions. She rapidly gained my trust and would go on to become a good friend and play a critical role supporting me in several ventures. For RVI, her first responsibilities were to find us a small office near Capitol Square in Madison, work with me and Lena Chow on a logo and basic image package, and create a rudimentary web presence for the company.

Over the next year we would take on a variety of consulting projects and invest in public companies involved in biotech tools, diagnostics, and devices before eventually raising a small venture fund. Creating and managing a fund wasn't something I had ever planned, but while raising capital for NimbleGen I became increasingly interested in what life was like on the other side of the table, investing in promising life science companies.

I recruited Dan Meyer to join me as a partner. I first met Dan when he was a venture associate at Point Judith Capital. He had been a math major at Middlebury and graduated from Dartmouth's Tuck School of Business. Originally from

Vermont, Dan was a straight shooter I could trust. He had good judgment and an appropriate degree of confidence, he loved his dogs, and he was experienced in the VC world.

Together we crafted a strategy for a fund we called the Black Swan Fund, taking the name from the 2007 book *The Black Swan*, by Nassim Nicholas Taleb, which explored the outsize impact of highly improbable events. Our pitch: to leverage my personal network and knowledge of the life science tools sector to invest in emerging but under-the-radar companies that could have a big impact. We planned to seek funding from large established life science companies, some of whom had internal venture capital groups but relied on small business development departments that needed help finding new opportunities.

Our target investors were sitting on plenty of capital. Part of our pitch was that by participating in the fund they would get early visibility on a portfolio of companies they might someday want to acquire. Potentially, they would be able to close an acquisition of strategic interest or benefit from the financial gain resulting from another company's acquisition. We wanted to keep the fund relatively small so that we could actively engage with the companies we invested in. Somewhere between $50 million and $200 million seemed to be the sweet spot.

We spent months researching the field, refining our pitch, meeting with early-stage companies, developing deal flow, reviewing business plans, and talking with senior executives at the large life science companies, as well as various family offices, large financial institutions, and university endowments. Somewhere along the way, we brought in Greg McGuinness to cover opportunities in Europe from his home office in the UK. Greg and I had worked together at Perkin-Elmer, Genetic MicroSystems, and NimbleGen. I trusted him and knew he enjoyed evaluating new technologies and business opportunities. Plus, he knew how to close a deal.

The reception to our pitch was quite positive. We made great contacts at new and established companies and developed a good understanding of the strategies of most of the major life science firms. Unfortunately, most companies interested in proceeding tried to convince us to work exclusively with them as scouts for merger-and-acquisition candidates. If a company we introduced was acquired, then we'd get paid a finder's fee. We tried this nonexclusively with one major private equity firm, but it really wasn't the business model we wanted to pursue.

One day a contact at the Wisconsin Alumni Research Foundation offered to introduce us to a venture capitalist we'll refer to as "Randy from Seattle," someone who had been investing in biotech companies for more than twenty years. They thought he might be helpful, and we happily accepted the offer. We drove to Chicago and spent an hour or so talking to Randy over coffee at the Hilton Chicago O'Hare while he was on a layover.

Our business model intrigued him, in part because he knew that the state of Wisconsin was giving money to venture firms willing to make investments in Badger State businesses, provided the VC had an office located there. Randy asked if we would consider joining forces. He'd put up some funding along with whatever we could get from the state and raise from others, and we'd manage our business as a subsidiary of his firm. This was completely unexpected and exciting. Before leaving to catch his flight, Randy invited us to his winter home in Key Largo, Florida, to spend a day talking through the plan in more detail.

A week or so later, Dan, Courtney, and I caught an early morning flight to Miami, picked up a rental car, and drove to the Keys. Randy's home was in an exclusive gated community called the Ocean Reef Club in Key Largo, at the northern tip of the Keys, just south of Homestead, Florida. They have a private air strip to make access easy for residents such as Randy, but we had to fly commercial. His home was an enormous concrete-and-glass structure obviously designed to withstand hurricanes. It was located at the mouth of a canal with sweeping views out to the Atlantic. There was a sizable dock with several large fishing boats and a few smaller Boston Whalers. Randy greeted us at the door wearing his trademark yellow polo shirt, shorts, and flip-flops, and invited us in for a lovely lunch prepared by his wife.

After introductions and informal chat, the conversation turned to his boat collection. Randy suggested we all head to the dock and go for a ride on one of the larger fishing vessels. We spent the next two hours on the water, heading south down the Keys. We took in the sun and the salty sea air and traded stories about fishing and various locations one might travel to from there, all the while enduring Randy's power display of wealth.

Upon returning to the house, we finally got down to business. Randy wanted us to merge RVI into his holding company and make us a subsidiary. He told us about the geographically focused subsidiaries he was setting up in the Middle East and in China, and he loved the idea of having a company in Madison since the state was about to provide funding to local VCs willing to make investments in Wisconsin. He was also excited about having an entity focused solely on tools and diagnostics. This all seemed too good to be true, but the part that was missing was what we would get out of it.

Randy kept beating around the bush on any actual details, instead sharing stories of all the money he was raising offshore, and how we could gain access to those sources of capital. Eventually he told us he thought he should keep 50 percent of the profits. So in exchange for giving us some brand recognition with his name and contacts, he wanted half our business. What's more, he expected us to raise most of the investment funds ourselves. That sounded pretty steep, and it changed the whole tone of the visit.

Trying to lighten the mood, Courtney asked Randy whether he actually owned all those boats down by the dock. With his wife clearing off the lunch table in the background, Randy replied, "Courtney, you know what they say. If it flies, floats, or fucks, rent it." She wasn't expecting that, and had no idea what to say next. In fact, he made all of us uncomfortable. His vagueness about the financial terms, his poor offer, his mysterious sources of funding, his general crudeness—we just weren't feeling it.

An hour or so later we thanked Randy and his wife for lunch and the boat ride, but we really needed to get back to the airport. We told him we'd seriously consider his proposal and that it would help to see something in writing. We weren't a hundred feet out of his driveway before we all agreed not to work with him. We'd made the right decision: a few years later Randy was indicted on charges of securities fraud, money laundering, and tax evasion; fined millions of dollars; saw his company go bankrupt; and spent several years in jail.

><><

KIDNEY FAILURE

One day in the spring of 2009, I went in for my regular kidney checkup, and Dr. Seifter was on vacation. The covering doctor was a pleasant-enough fellow, and I knew the routine by heart. When my visit came to an end, after the students had felt my cystic kidneys, the conversation with the doctor deviated significantly from the usual script. "You know, Stan, your creatinine is continuing to rise," he said, "and while it's not a problem at the moment, I think this would be a good time to start learning about what's involved in a kidney transplant."

I hadn't seen this coming. Dr. Seifter had consistently told me that every PKD patient is different, that I might never need a transplant, and that we should just keep an eye on it. Sure, my creatinine was rising, and so was my blood pressure, but that was being effectively managed with meds. So I asked, "What are you suggesting?"

"I think it would be a good idea for you to contact one of our transplant coordinators. You and your wife could meet with them and just learn what's involved. That way, should you ever need to go down this path, it's not a complete mystery. Does that make sense to you?"

"Sure," I replied, "just let me know who to contact."

A few weeks later Elise and I met with a transplant

coordinator, a woman with a comforting manner. It was as if we were meeting a therapist or counselor. We sat across from one another, Elise and I on a cushy couch and the co-ordinator in a leather chair. She explained the transplant process at a high level. How there are living donors and de-ceased donors. How you could get on a national list to be considered as a recipient of a deceased donor ("the list"), but if you could find a living donor, then those kidneys generally lasted twice as long.

Whether sourced from a living or deceased donor, the kidney had to be compatible with me. Compatibility was mostly a matter of having a matching blood type, since the newest immunosuppressant drugs were so effective that they could prevent rejection even with a less-than-ideally-matched donor. It was no longer the case that one needed to find a perfectly matched kidney donor.

Living donors had to be tested to be sure they were suit-able, which meant they were healthy enough to donate one of their two kidneys. The likelihood that they might need both had to be extremely low. If one is found suitable, the donation process is safe, with serious adverse events occur-ring only on the order of one in ten thousand donors.

This was all interesting, but at some point I interrupted the coordinator and said, "I don't mean to be rude or any-thing. This is all really helpful. But I honestly only have two questions."

"Oh," she said. "Well, what would you like to know?"

"First, how soon do you think I'll need a transplant? And second, how long does a transplanted kidney last?"

The coordinator started flipping through a folder of my medical records. "I haven't studied your case that closely yet," she said, "so give me a minute to review your notes." She flipped through a few more pages and then looked up at me. "Again, I'd really need more time to consider this, but on first impression I'd say six months."

My jaw dropped.

"Excuse me," I said. "Are you saying I'll need a transplant in six months?"

"Yes, that's what it appears from what I'm seeing here."

"But Dr. Seifter told me three months ago that I might never need a transplant! How is this possible?"

I was devastated. For seven years now Elise and I had done our best to make the most out of life. It was easy to forget our alarm at that original PKD diagnosis in 2002. We seriously thought I'd be one of those lucky 50 percent of PKD patients that never need a transplant.

I had effectively compartmentalized my visions of worst-case scenarios so really hadn't considered what a transplant might mean for my life. I hadn't begun to think about the process of finding an organ donor. Not to mention living on immunosuppressant drugs for the rest of my life! Would I be a bubble boy? Would I be able to continue enjoying all the things I like to do now? Could I continue to eat and drink what I wanted? To travel the world? So many questions.

We didn't get to my second question about how long a kidney is good for. I'd later learn that a deceased donor kidney, on average, would continue to function adequately for seven to ten years. A living donor kidney might last twice as long. But there is an extremely large range of outcomes, with some kidneys not making it more than a few years and others lasting thirty or more.

Elise was speechless, but as soon as we got home, she

urged me to call Peter Harris at Mayo Clinic. She wasn't
going to simply accept the transplant coordinator's con-
clusion. I called Peter and he invited me to Rochester,
Minnesota, to get a second opinion from their leading
transplant nephrologist. We were able to set up that visit
quickly, and a week later I went to Mayo for two full days of
intensive testing.

At the end of the second day, I sat down with the nephrologist to review my results. He looked up from his desk
after reviewing all my files and said, "Stan, there is no doubt
that you have PKD and that it is progressing. I agree with the
team in Boston. You will likely need a transplant, though I
have to say that I would be shocked if you needed one as
soon as six months from now."

I breathed a sigh of relief.

"On the other hand," he continued, "I'd also be shocked
if you did not need one in two years. So this would be a good
time to start talking with various transplant programs,
thinking about where you would want the procedure performed, and beginning to work on finding a living donor."

I wasn't thrilled with the news, but at least I now had a
degree of clarity. I also had a bit more time to come to terms
with what was happening. I needed to start making plans, to
speak with several transplant programs, and to learn from
others who had been down this path. Many questions remained, but getting answers became my top priority. Who
would be my donor? Would anyone?! Where would I get a
transplant procedure performed? What about my career
going forward? What about my life?!

As unexpected as all this was, there was little we could
do at the moment, so we returned home to St. John and

tried to process everything. As we disembarked the plane in St. Thomas, the warm, humid air and the light tropical trade winds enveloped us. After taxiing to the ferry dock, we boarded the boat and settled in for the short ride home. I gazed into the blue hues of Pillsbury Sound as we made the crossing. Hypnotic and relaxing, the ride made it easy to put the reality of PKD and a transplant out of my mind. At least for the moment.

✕✕✕

TRANSPLANT

After my Mayo Clinic visit, I slowly began to focus more seriously on preparing for a kidney transplant and winding down my activities at Rose Ventures. I wanted to keep the entity alive, but I was in no shape to continue the road warrior life associated with constant fundraising and evaluating potential investment opportunities. I helped Dan and Greg segue into other opportunities but continued to keep the RVI legal entity alive with Courtney staffing the office in Madison. I had no idea what life would be like posttransplant or whether I'd even continue to use RVI at all, but it just seemed premature to completely shut it down.

Realizing there was minimal access to medical care on St. John, we began thinking about finding a home base up north for this next chapter in our lives. We had never completely severed our roots with the Boston area, and all our serious medical care was based there. Elise had become a trustee of the Marine Biological Laboratory / University of Chicago, a prestigious biological research institution in Woods Hole, Massachusetts. Located on the southwestern tip of Cape Cod, Woods Hole is roughly ninety minutes south of Boston by car. We found a second house there on a pond and began to settle in.

My two biggest issues now were finding a living donor and deciding where to have the transplant performed. Even though my PKD care had been at the Brigham, I was shaken by the way I had come to learn that I would need a transplant much sooner than expected. If I were going to purchase anything of value, I'd shop around to find the best product. I decided to apply that same attitude to transplant programs.

Over a month or so I visited with Mayo in Rochester, UW in Madison, and Tufts, Beth Israel, Mass General, and the Brigham in Boston. The person who had the most influence on my decision was Dr. Hans Sollinger, who at the time led the program at UW. A kind older man who spoke with a slight German accent, he advised me that all the major programs in the US had capable surgeons and could perform the actual transplant with similar outcomes. What I should really focus on, in his opinion, was the after-transplant care. Which program had transplant nephrologists and coordinators I trusted and felt comfortable interacting with regularly? Where would I prefer to go to have blood samples drawn frequently to monitor my health? These questions helped me form a new perspective I hadn't considered and made me realize I should have the transplant done in Boston.

The decision made, I quickly settled on Beth Israel, where Dr. Martha Pavlakis was the lead transplant nephrologist. I continued to see Dr. Seifter and the transplant group at the Brigham in parallel, as I discovered that insurance companies limit the number of donors who can be worked up at one time in one program, and this is a time-consuming process. While all the tests could be done in a week in principle, inefficiencies in scheduling and logistics typically drag this out many months. The benefit of having multiple donors worked up simultaneously at different programs is obvious.

Finding a living donor was another surprising and eye-opening experience. I was shocked and flattered at the number of family and friends who offered to donate. Unfortunately the vast majority of willing donors were not suitable candidates. Transplant programs are cautious in evaluating living donors and take organs only from people healthy enough to endure a lifetime with just one kidney. One by one, week by week, potential donors were crossed off the list.

Because of the great response my close family and friends had given me, I didn't publicize my need for a kidney as quickly and broadly as I should have. I must admit I was a bit embarrassed about asking for help. Years later a living donor advocate named Harvey Mysel gave me a different view on this whole process. A two-time transplant recipient himself, Harvey pointed out that most donors are people that the recipient wouldn't even expect. As a consequence, the best way to approach the search is not by asking someone to donate, but rather by making people aware of your need for a lifesaving transplant—as broadly as possible—and then allowing your donor to find you.

This was exactly my experience. Nearly a year had gone by. Elise and a few other family members were still being evaluated. I was beginning to feel the consequences of my failing kidneys. It showed up first in the form of increasing blood pressure, which was easily controlled with medications. Things started to get uncomfortable when I began to feel fatigue and regular muscle cramping. My body was sending me a signal. Around this time, I received a phone call from Darren Lee, a friend of mine from work. We had met back in 1990, in the heyday of the PCR business, and had shared many work and life experiences that would all make for good stories.

I had recently told Darren in passing about my need for a kidney, while attending a Red Sox game together. I later learned he had started talking to mutual friends, mostly from our days together at Perkin-Elmer, and they had begun getting evaluated as possible donors. Darren himself turned out to be a perfect match. His phone call to tell me this was truly unexpected, both in content and tone.

"How could you not ask me to be your donor?!" he scolded me. "You know I'm the same blood type as you. I'm healthy, and we can get this done quickly. What's wrong with you?!"

"Sorry, Darren. I just wasn't comfortable broadcasting my need. I thought I might find a suitable and compatible donor from a relative. There are still a few being evaluated."

"Well, get me into the process!" he insisted.

From that day, things moved quickly. Darren was absolutely correct. He was an ideal donor and, remarkably, a perfect "six-point HLA" genetic match too.

The few months before my transplant were a blur as I was trying to figure out what to do about my business while also dealing with my dad's passing in December 2010, which hit me hard. After spending Thanksgiving with my sister Audrey in California, he'd fallen ill, winding up on dialysis and other forms of life support as organ after organ began to fail. Fortunately for him the end came quickly. Both of my sisters and I were there by his side for those final days. The last words I heard him say were "It sure was fun while it lasted."

In the aftermath my sisters and I had to handle the final disposition of his body, will, finances, house, belongings, and memorial service. My sisters were extremely helpful in handling the fallout of Dad's passing, but I really felt the burden of it all. At the same time I was also preparing for my transplant. I'm fortunate that my skills at multitasking and mental compartmentalization have always been so good.

The actual transplant occurred on January 18, 2011, and went very smoothly. At least it did for me. Darren was up and about the next day, which is pretty typical. A week or so later, however, his groin became inflamed, and he had to undergo a second surgery to resolve the problem. This is not typical. Aside from his friends' endless ribbing about his big swollen balls—ribbing I'm sure he actually enjoyed—his bigger concern was that this complication had delayed by a few months his plans to train for the golf season. After the fact, Darren would claim the postponement was no big deal compared with saving a friend's life and that the transplant was one of the most rewarding experiences of his life. I'm glad he feels that way, and I am eternally grateful to him.

I was never concerned about the surgery. I probably didn't give the surgeons enough credit, as I had this simplistic mental model of the transplant being similar to the installation of a new fuel filter in a car. You don't even take out the old one! You just open up the hood (abdomen), put the new one in place, hook it up to the input line (the artery), output line (the vein), and drainage line (the bladder), and close it up. A life spent on immunosuppressant drugs was what worried me.

I stayed in an apartment we rented in Brookline for the first few months, close to Beth Israel Deaconess Medical Center. I needed to visit the hospital for frequent blood draws, and I wanted to be close by in case complications arose. It was January and February in Boston, and a particularly snowy winter, so I rarely went outside. Besides Elise, I had few visitors. My sister Diane flew up to help out for a while. We kept face masks and Purell on a table by the apartment door. Fortunately there was a small gym in the building, so I would go down and walk on the treadmill as part of my surgical rehab program.

I was told that I could probably start working from home in a few weeks but that it would take a few months to recover from the surgery. I wasn't in terrible pain, but I needed to get used to a new routine that involved blood monitoring, many medications (mostly to prevent graft rejection), and gaining greater awareness of what I touched, ate, and inhaled. They had warned me that the first six months were critical, so I was extremely careful at first. Once I started getting used to the new routine and going outside into the world again, I became determined to keep pushing back toward some sense of normalcy.

It felt as if the next two years were largely about expanding my boundaries. The first milestone was a walk along Beacon Street's snow-covered sidewalks and entering a grocery store; the second, a trolley ride on the "T" to Boston

Garden for a Celtics game. The car was packed with people and full of germs. The Garden crowd was screaming and spewing aerosols into the air all night. But I survived and felt an enormous sense of relief and optimism.

I took my first flight on a plane in March. As I boarded, I was too embarrassed to put a mask on but immediately donned it when I heard someone cough a few minutes after taking my seat. I thought I looked silly wearing it, but I sat back, closed my eyes, and felt the tension melt away.

By June I was back to working normally again. One day I was walking along Avenue of the Americas in Midtown Manhattan, marveling at the crowds making their way among the towering skyscrapers, when my phone rang. The caller ID said "Transplant Center," so I ducked into a building entryway for some privacy and answered. It was my transplant coordinator calling to tell me that they wanted me to stop taking one of my immunosuppressants immediately. They had run a routine blood test using PCR and detected concerning levels of a virus called BK. This virus is present in 80–90 percent of people, but if you have a normally functioning immune system it remains inactive. Mine was now replicating, and BK is known to attack the bladder and kidney.

There were no known effective treatments for BK. The only option was to reduce immunosuppression—at the risk of having your body reject the transplanted kidney—and hope that your immune system killed off the virus before your immune system did too much damage to the graft. It took about nine months of living on reduced immunosuppression before the BK was below detectable levels.

In the old days tests to detect a BK flare did not exist,

which invariably led to loss of the transplanted organ. But thanks to PCR, the technology I had helped bring to the marketplace, the virus could now be routinely screened for and detected at low levels so that one could intervene in time to save the graft. The same PCR test could monitor how effectively your body was fighting off the virus once immunosuppression had been reduced. Imagine the odds— the technology I had helped bring to the clinic had played a role in saving my own transplanted kidney!

The culmination of my comeback came on a safari in Kenya and Tanzania with a group of Elise's friends and colleagues from the Marine Biological Laboratory. Midway through the adventure we slept in a tent in the Serengeti National Park, hours away from any real medical care and days from a transplant program. Armed guards were stationed around the campground, all night on the watch for lions or other wild animals. I remember looking out of the tent at the stars, smelling the air, listening to the sounds of untouched Africa, and feeling an immense sense of peacefulness, contentment, and achievement.

Shortly after we returned to Woods Hole, Elise was walking down the beach and ran into a man with a beautiful black Labrador retriever. We were still grieving the passing of our male dog Rowley, a Lab-shepherd mix who had loved gorilla dolls and had been my companion through my first start-up experience. The man told her about a breeder in the Northeast Kingdom in Vermont, with whom we ultimately connected and visited.

Just as my donor found me, so did a beautiful black Labrador find us. As we sat in the living room of the kennel's main house, he came bounding down the stairs, crossed the room, wiggled his way around the coffee table and pushed the other pups aside. In no uncertain terms he said, "Please take *me!*" We did in fact take him, and we named him Burke, for the town in which the kennel is located. We later nicknamed him "Burkeley" for fun, and as a reminder of our life in California. Burke was full of love and became my best friend, nursing me back to health through daily walks for years to come.

I was ready to move on with my life, eager for the next adventure. Both Elise and I missed St. John immensely, but it would be more than a year before we could even go back for a visit. At some point the reality sunk in that I couldn't go back to living in such a remote location given my need to be near a transplant program, so our part-time living arrangement in Woods Hole would become full time. This was hardly a concession, as we had a beautiful home just a short walk to the beach, from which we could watch the sun set over the water to the west.

This would be a good place to retire, but I wasn't yet ready for that. To the contrary, reminded of my mortality, I sensed a degree of urgency. I had unfinished business and needed to decide what to focus on next. Bob Palay had introduced me to a transplant surgeon friend in Chicago who was organizing a foundation to raise funds to help address the severe organ supply shortage. I had never considered leading this kind of philanthropic fundraising, and it was certainly a worthy cause. At the same time Courtney was still working as my executive associate at Rose Ventures. She had been handling incoming inquiries and assisting me in developing a number of trial balloon business plans, but I hadn't committed to any new plan yet and wasn't even sure I wanted to. Then one day in December 2012, I opened an email from my donor friend, Darren.

10

GENOMIC DIAGNOSTICS

Ideas for new companies can come from anywhere, at any time. Sometimes an unexpected epiphany makes all the difference. A nugget of an idea brews over time and incubates, and one's brain slowly pieces the puzzle together before reaching that aha moment. Other times one has a passion to address some topic of interest, comes up with an idea, and spends weeks, months, or years seeing if one can develop it far enough to justify starting a company. And some of those ideas get to the point where the founders smile at one another and say, "Woo-hoo! It works! We've got a business!" But sometimes ideas just appear, nearly fully formed, with no warning, and one needs to decide whether it is really a worthy pursuit or a distraction that could lead to loss of time, money, relationships, and energy that could have been spent on other opportunities.

My next company was based on such an idea, an

unexpected opportunity that felt right the moment it appeared, and I hoped it wouldn't wind up a fool's errand. I wasn't looking to start a new company, and hadn't previously thought to solve this particular problem. All of that changed when my kidney donor, Darren, pointed me to an article about biomarkers in transplantation from the December 2012 issue of *Clinical Laboratory News.*

I was almost two years posttransplant at this point and doing well. Most of the lifestyle changes required of me had become routine, including the twenty-plus pills a day, the frequent handwashing, and occasional mask wearing. None of this interfered with my professional activities, which involved a mix of consulting projects and serving on several boards. I was happy to be on my own, not working for anyone else, thrilled to have overcome the riskiest part of my kidney transplant journey, and perfectly content with my care. I had never considered how my doctors were monitoring my health. I didn't question the underlying rationale for their tests; the quality of the data; or if, why, and how those tests might be improved.

As the biomarkers paper made clear, the standard of care for kidney transplant recipients involved periodically monitoring serum creatinine (from every week early posttransplant to every few months later on). Creatinine is an indicator of renal function. As with golf, the lower the score, the better the player is doing. What I didn't realize is that a rise in serum creatinine is a nonspecific result with respect to rejection. There are several other things that might cause creatinine to rise and are not nearly as concerning.

So if things were going well, a patient's serum creatinine

level would remain relatively low and fairly stable over time. A sudden rise of 20 percent or more could be caused by rejection, or by other, less serious conditions. Creatinine spikes were often used as triggers to perform an "indication" or "for cause" biopsy. The procedure involves sticking a needle into the transplanted kidney and withdrawing a few chunks of tissue. The sample is then stained with certain dyes and examined under a microscope to determine whether the real culprit is rejection.

The big problem with monitoring creatinine levels, apart from lack of specificity, is that it is a late-trailing indicator of damage already done. As transplant nephrologist Dr. Dan Salomon used to say, it's like watching a house on fire and the fire alarm goes off only when half the house is already destroyed. For more than a decade, researchers had been looking for alternative markers in blood that might provide an early and specific indication that rejection was occurring, before the damage was done. Hypothetically, if one could find a noninvasive indicator of subclinical or "silent" rejection (i.e., rejection occurring in advance of any clinical signs such as elevated creatinine), an early intervention to modify immunosuppressive drug levels could possibly extend the transplanted kidney's life.

In 2021, three quarters of a million Americans suffered from renal failure, with one hundred and forty thousand of them waiting on the organ transplant list for a kidney from a deceased donor. Only twenty-five thousand transplants were performed in the US that year (just under six thousand from living donors), while another forty thousand people were added to the waiting list. The need for more living donors is thus urgent, as is an optimized process for dealing with deceased donor kidneys and methods for extending the life of already-implanted organs.

The *Clinical Laboratory News* article made three things immediately obvious to me. First, my doctors had no idea how well I was doing at any point in time. They were just waiting to see signs that I was sick, and then they would react.

Second, there were two hundred thousand kidney transplant recipients like me living in the US, and three times that many globally. If they were all monitored with a test run four times a year, that's a potential market opportunity of more than a million tests each year. Given that the alternative was potential loss of life or the start of an expensive and exhausting dialysis regimen, a new blood test with the right performance would be attractive at a high enough price to justify development and commercialization.

Third, I strongly believed this was a solvable problem. Genomic markers had to exist in blood or urine, most likely in the form of gene-expression levels that could be measured and provide the kind of early warning signal the field needed. Many such markers were in fact being studied, as noted in the review Darren sent me, but it was challenging to get large numbers of transplant patients enrolled in studies. The available data was limited and not yet particularly convincing.

A test that addressed this opportunity would greatly benefit my own life, as well as the lives of other transplant recipients. I instantly concluded that there was nothing more important that I might devote my time to. My entire career seemed to have prepared me to address it. I just needed to learn more about what was really going on in this field. For all I knew, someone could have already solved the problem since that review had been written. Alternatively, multiple competitive groups might have gotten close to a solution, and if I wanted to get involved, I'd need to decide which group of clinicians and scientists I'd like to work with.

In exploring the philanthropic fundraising opportunity related to solving the organ supply shortage, I had met a surgeon who directed the transplant program at Northwestern Medicine, Dr. Michael Abecassis. I knew Mike was well connected in the transplant field, having been a past president of the American Society of Transplant Surgeons. He is a smart guy, and I enjoyed interacting with him, so I emailed him asking what he thought of this opportunity. Less than five minutes later he called me.

"Stan. Great to hear from you. The short answer is 'Yes and yes.' This is really important stuff. In fact, I've been working on this along with a collaborator of mine at Scripps for several years now, and we've been awarded over $25 million in funding from the NIH to address the problem. We're involved in the largest study of its kind, looking at a collection of blood gene-expression profiles we discovered using Affymetrix microarrays. We have twelve transplant programs participating, with three hundred patients recruited, each providing samples every three months for two years. What's more, we're doing biopsies at several time points so we have gold standard controls to compare with.

"There are several other groups out there, but nobody else is close. Some are talking a big game, but when you look closely at the data, either there isn't really very much or the study designs are flawed. So we're pretty confident.

In fact, we've been talking about starting a company and finding a CEO, and also talking about partnering with Life Technologies."

Life Tech was the biggest life science tools company in the field, and many of their senior people had worked at Perkin-Elmer or ABI, so I knew them well. Similarly, I knew many of the key people at Affymetrix, on whose platform this test would be run.

"Well, I'm extremely interested in that CEO role," I replied. "We should talk. And please don't sign any deal with Life Tech before we do. In fact, if you don't mind, maybe I can join you for your next meeting with them."

Mike suggested I meet his partner, Dr. Dan Salomon, and with that we were off and running. I flew to San Diego a few days later to meet Dan at Scripps. Dan was a laid-back California-surfer type who enjoyed working with new technologies. His personality was very different from that of Mike, who, being a surgeon from Chicago, was always direct and commanding. A transplant nephrologist and first-class genomics scientist, Dan was more quiet, thoughtful, and persuasive in his approach. That said, they both were extremely productive, were complementary in terms of skills, and enjoyed working together.

I sat in Dan's office drinking from a fire hose as he tutored me in the essentials of transplant medicine. Dan drew all sorts of flowcharts on his whiteboard. First he taught me the basics of renal transplantation. Then biomarkers and the technologies he was employing to analyze transplant-patient blood samples. And finally his view of the business opportunities.

The personal chemistry among the three of us was

excellent, so two weeks later I returned to join them for a meeting at Life Tech headquarters a half hour north of San Diego in Carlsbad. Life Tech turned out to be sincerely interested in doing something together that involved funding research in exchange for equity, but I continued to urge Mike and Dan to slow down and avoid selling this off cheap. We hadn't even created a legal entity yet!

The meeting convinced us that this work had value. Life Tech had validated that. That day we all agreed to start a company, and on March 21, 2013, we formally incorporated as Transplant Genomics Inc. (TGI). We opened a bank account, seeded it with $250,000 of our own money, and issued founders stock. Most of the first year was spent developing and refining our plans, with me learning about the business aspects of renal transplantation, including key players and arcane regulatory and reimbursement issues. In turn, they followed my lead on how to build and grow a start-up.

By early 2014 we had a solid plan, including our initial target product specifications, a road map of value-enhancing milestones in the development and commercialization process, a good sense of the competitive environment, an option to an exclusive license covering the key IP to which we needed rights (owned jointly by Scripps and Northwestern), and partnerships with some key opinion leaders in the space. We were now ready to talk with serious institutional investors.

Given our reputations in our respective fields, we felt good about our prospects. We were completely unprepared, however, for how the traditional venture investor was viewing new start-ups focused on molecular diagnostics (MDx). In particular, those focused on the organ transplant field.

Our first challenge was following in the wake of a slew of MDx companies that had secured funding between 2000 and 2013. Most had built up big commercial organizations before their product launch, only to see holdups in securing reimbursement. Millions of dollars were burned on marketing and sales organizations idled while awaiting approval to sell their product. The typical company needed to raise at least $25 million to complete their discovery work, another $25 million to finish the studies required to secure a reimbursement decision (so the test would be paid for!), and $25 million to launch the test and drive adoption. That was a best-case scenario. Many companies had to raise $150–$200 million. We were telling investors we could get all this done with just $25 million.

The second challenge was that the goalposts kept moving for securing reimbursement from the Centers for Medicare & Medicaid Services (CMS). There was frequent turnover of leadership, and each time a new director came on board or a new regulation was put in place, MDx companies had to burn precious cash paying commercial staff to sit and do nothing while they modified their plans to be in compliance. Of those MDx companies that did manage to get reimbursement, some didn't get a high enough price approved to support their cost structure and had to close shop. Those who did get a favorable level of reimbursement struggled with driving adoption with skeptical physicians always seeking more data. Some built successful businesses that wound up providing liquidity to their investors in the form of an IPO or acquisition, yet the valuations were not high enough to justify the investments.

Of course we believed we were different, and we had

compelling arguments. Over $25 million in NIH grant funding had already been spent on development, so the first chunk of funding was already in place and was nondilutive to new investors. We also showed how we would have a fundamental cost structure that was so low that we could be profitable even on a low level of reimbursement. In addition, we were addressing a highly concentrated market, with tests being performed for doctors at just 150–200 transplant centers. This would enable us to address the market with a small commercial organization, for which we planned to hold off on staffing until we neared a reimbursed test to sell. But in the end the VCs had endured such a difficult time in the MDx market over the prior decade that they just weren't willing to dip their toes back in the water.

As if this was not bad enough, the Theranos saga was unfolding in real time just as we were starting our business. It ended in lawsuits, bankruptcy, and jail time for CEO Elizabeth Holmes and company, along with newspaper accounts, books, and movies. The suspicion of more widespread fraud in the diagnostics industry further challenged fundraising for start-up diagnostic companies.

The final dagger was the fact that two somewhat comparable transplant diagnostic companies had burned investors in the past with similar stories as ours. They used different technologies, but they looked great on paper. Big-name VC firms invested, products were brought to market, but in the end they failed when physicians decided the tests either had not been properly validated or didn't provide useful information. The VCs took a beating and had zero interest in investing in another transplant diagnostics company.

When we started TGI we never imagined that the whole

MDx sector would be viewed as toxic and we would be unable to raise money from VCs. We had to think differently about funding this venture. Instead, we turned our attention to wealthy individual angel investors, family offices, and strategic corporate investors. Enough of them liked what they saw to entrust us with their money and give us a chance to pursue our mission. After all, our vision, story, people, and plan were really solid!

I was convinced we could make this work, and willing to risk my reputation and my own money on it. I knew plenty of high-net-worth individuals who had invested with me before and were willing to take a bet with me again. They knew they had a leader who would work as hard as possible, who would be transparent with them and seek their help if needed, and who had previously delivered for them multiple times.

The remaining source of available funding came from companies and other organizations with a strategic interest in transplant diagnostics. A group of a half dozen well-financed acquirers were ready to take our business forward if we could prove the test worked, get our tests reimbursed by Medicare, and show signs of adoption from KOLs. Raising the money we needed may have taken longer and required much greater effort than we anticipated, but by late 2014 we had our first few million. By 2015 we had substantially more, as well as some influential investors. Now it was up to us to deliver on our promises.

$\times\!\!\times\!\!\times$

GROWING A VIRTUAL COMPANY

With three founders living in different parts of the country, our first big decision was where to establish our headquarters. I was living on Cape Cod, Mike in Chicago, and Dan in Southern California. We concluded that Massachusetts made the most sense, based on my location, its ready access to relevant talent and support infrastructure, and its strong start-up investment community. I had a spare apartment just outside of Boston, which we used as our initial corporate address. We tentatively planned to designate space in Dan's lab at Scripps as "the TGI lab," but I was skeptical about putting this into practice, especially once we reached the commercial stage. Having Scripps as a partner/landlord would have introduced all sorts of conflicts and complications. For the time being we didn't need to make any firm decisions regarding the clinical lab.

We took a very unconventional approach to research and development. Since Mike and Dan had already secured over $25 million in NIH grant funds—with any IP they developed being subject to a license I was negotiating with Scripps and Northwestern—we felt that trying to duplicate their capabilities and activities in a separate laboratory would be pointless. I knew that VCs would instinctively hate this idea, in large part because the company wouldn't control either product development or longer-term research. Nonetheless, I was convinced that our goals were aligned and that the development milestones critical to the company would be addressed in a timely manner under Mike and Dan's direction. I pitched this arrangement as a huge benefit to new investors, as the discovery work would get done at no cost to them, saving us from having to raise $25 million. What's more, we'd get to market faster by leveraging all the expertise, access to special equipment, unique blood samples and related clinical documentation, and work previously completed.

We relied heavily on trusted relationships to handle our outsourced legal work and marketing communications program. Courtney, Pete, and Darren joined us and filled out our core management team in operations, finance, and marketing. We quickly secured licenses and sponsored research agreements with Scripps and Northwestern, ensuring access to past and new IP developed at those sites.

An old friend from Affymetrix had warned me that reimbursement was everything in the diagnostics business. If you don't have it, you have nothing of value. As a consequence, you should focus on reimbursement as the primary objective of your business strategy and build your entire plan around the shortest path to securing a coverage decision at an attractive level of reimbursement per test.

With this in mind, Mike suggested we meet with Rob Webb, a good friend of his and the former CEO of Optum. Mike was an advisor to Optum, a division of United Health Group—the leading commercial insurer for transplants. Optum managed more than half the transplants performed in the US.

The three of us met at Rob's Minneapolis office to introduce the business concept to him and teach me about the business aspects of kidney transplants. The most important thing I learned that day was that Medicare provides primary coverage for the majority of kidney transplants in the US. It thus became apparent that if CMS approved coverage and set an acceptable price point for reimbursement, roughly two-thirds of our tests would be paid for. Rapidly obtaining a coverage decision from CMS drove all our decisions from that point on.

Mike knew nearly all the transplant program directors, as most were surgeons by training. When the American Transplant Congress was held in Seattle in mid-2013, Mike reserved a small conference room and invited the directors of ten of the most prominent transplant programs in the US to meet me and hear the story of our new company. We pitched our test as a new tool to enable early noninvasive detection of silent subclinical rejection, without the need to perform a biopsy. What's more, it would be a tool developed for the transplant community by the transplant community. We wanted them to join us as collaborators and early access partners. In return they would receive tests, participate in studies before commercial launch, and have a chance to speak in public or publish papers on their groundbreaking work.

In contrast to our early interactions with VCs, our attempts to raise money from angel investors familiar with at least one of the three founders turned out fruitful. We each had strong reputations for success and our own networks of wealthy individuals to back us. We also had clear personal motivations for developing a successful test. And we backed up our words by putting our skin in the game. All three founders invested amounts meaningful with respect to their personal net worth. I led several of the rounds and invested in all of them.

The downside of this approach is that it forced us to continually raise relatively small amounts of money,

$2–$5 million per round, with individual investments per round ranging from tens to hundreds of thousands. It also created an administrative burden by requiring us to interface with a large number of investors. It was effective, however, and we successfully assembled a sophisticated group of financial backers who could really help us grow. They brought not only money but personal experience and networks in life sciences, diagnostics, transplantation, insurance, reimbursement, finance, operations, and other relevant disciplines.

By mid-2014 we had secured a license from Scripps and Northwestern, put in place sponsored research agreements with both institutions providing access to new IP and knowhow, raised initial funding, developed relationships with collaborating KOL transplant programs, and begun to build and promote our brand. We next turned our focus to refining our product, developing data, and performing small-scale clinical studies in preparation for initiating the CMS reimbursement process. We also began building relationships with other groups of strategic value. One notable relationship was with Affymetrix, whose platform we were using to perform our test.

I already had many contacts within the company, and I had known their CEO, Frank Witney, from years ago when he led Packard Biosciences (and Darren had worked for him). We visited with Frank in Santa Clara, gave a presentation of our past work and future plans, and proposed a mutually beneficial collaboration that would showcase the capabilities of the Affymetrix platform in molecular diagnostics.

Specifically, if Frank would agree to place two array-based

analytical systems in Dan's lab in La Jolla and provide us with the reagents and consumables we needed, we would analyze hundreds of transplant recipients with their products, publish the data jointly with Affymetrix, and publicly demonstrate the value of the Affymetrix platform as a clinical diagnostic tool. The marketing and promotional value to them would more than offset the cost of providing materials to us. Frank agreed. The benefit to TGI was saving millions of dollars on equipment, reagents, and associated consumables (specialized tubes, et cetera) we'd otherwise have to purchase, which is the kind of opportunity a start-up CEO always needs to be seeking. We soon issued a press release that benefited both companies: our brand, and their stock price.

As the prospect of moving to commercial stage became closer to reality, it was time to set up a CLIA-certified laboratory separate from Dan's lab at Scripps. CMS regulates all laboratory testing (except research) performed on humans in the US through the Clinical Laboratory Improvement Amendments (CLIA). Applying for licensure from the state and certification from CMS under CLIA were prerequisites to performing diagnostic testing, and we needed to find someone with experience in both of these areas.

An advisor suggested we hire a consultant they knew who could help us find the right people and also find shared lab space at another diagnostics company. It was commonplace for large labs to lease excess space and then sublease portions to smaller groups. The consultant was Michael McNulty, who had led Agilent's diagnostics business and, before that, had spent years working in the SmithKline and later Quest Diagnostics organizations. Michael knew all the key players in the clinical laboratory industry.

We met with Michael in the presidential suite at the Marriott Marquis in San Francisco in June 2014. The annual meeting of the American Society of Transplantation was taking place there, and Dan Salomon was serving as its president that year. We rapidly reached agreement, and over the next few months we looked at space Michael found in Boston and the San Francisco Bay Area. Boston made sense because we had a core management team there. The Bay Area made sense because of its concentrated venture capital activity, proximity to talent in Silicon Valley and the Peninsula, and dense base of West Coast customers. Nobody had a strong preference as we were all used to working remotely.

After a few months Michael surprised us. He was helping another company build out space in Pleasanton, in the East Bay, and asked us if we'd like a lab custom designed for us in the same space and ready to be occupied by year end. He could even get this space at a cheaper rate than on the Peninsula. The new location would also be attractive to employees, who could live in more affordable East Bay communities and avoid commuting across the bay. We never saw that one coming, but we jumped at the opportunity!

We didn't get the lab completed by the end of 2014, but we were able to occupy the space early in 2015. Indeed, everything takes longer than planned. As our VP of finance Pete Lewis used to always remind me, "All models are wrong; they're just models." They are tools that help you consider options. In most cases the best a model can do is provide guidance on how to move forward and serve as a baseline for future reassessment.

Michael found a great core team of certified lab

scientists and junior technicians to work for us. They were all cross-trained with the scientists in Dan's lab at Scripps. Once convinced that the interlab concordance data was satisfactory, we were almost ready to start offering testing services "for research purposes only." We still had to get our documentation in place and pass inspection and certification by the State of California first. Fortunately our lab director, Deirdre "Dede" Pierry, had been through the process many times before and was able to complete it smoothly and efficiently.

As we proceeded through 2015, our biggest surprise was having the opportunity to hire a seasoned chief medical officer. Mike Abecassis called me out of the blue and said, "Stan, I think we have a great shot to bring a real all-star onto the team. This isn't widely known yet, but Roy First is about to retire from his job at Astellas. You know I've been an advisor to Astellas for years, right? Do you know Roy?"

"No."

"Okay, well, he's a former transplant-center director. He was at the University of Cincinnati. He's a past president of the American Society of Transplantation, so he has a phenomenal network. Trust me on this, everyone loves Roy. He left Cincinnati to join Astellas, where he led the team that developed ProGraf. That's the brand name for tacrolimus. It's the leading immunosuppressant drug on the market. You must be taking it."

"Yes, I know tac. I was taking it. I switched to sirolimus a few years ago, but I'm aware that ProGraf has been the leader for years."

"Yes, well, it's going off patent soon, and it looks as if

Astellas has lost interest in the transplant field. They're re-focusing their efforts on oncology. Roy has no interest in staying on for this new chapter—which could be good news for us."

"But how do you know he's even interested in us?"

"I don't. That's why you should go meet him the day he resigns. I just don't believe he's ready to retire, and being at the forefront of the next big thing in transplant patient management could get his attention. You need to make the pitch before anyone else gets to him."

Roy and I exchanged emails, had a pleasant phone call, and a week later I flew to O'Hare to meet him for drinks the very afternoon he left Astellas. I was immediately put at ease when Roy walked in wearing a black leather biker's jacket, a big smile on his face, and wind-blown gray hair that made him look like Albert Einstein. We spent a few hours trading stories and getting to know each other, and by the time I was ready to catch my return flight that evening he had agreed to join the team. This was a real coup for us. Roy is respected by everyone in the field. Of course we issued a press release, and it created quite a buzz in the little world of transplantation, which was the only world that mattered to us.

Earlier in 2015, Mike, Dan, and John Friedewald—the key transplant nephrologist working with Mike at Northwestern and a founding scientific advisor to TGI—gave a talk about our new test at the Cutting Edge of Transplantation, an exclusive scientific meeting held annually in Phoenix. The meeting's name says it all. Speaking of names, by this time we had come up with a brand name for our test: the TruGraf blood gene-expression test. The group spoke about different aspects of TruGraf and caught the attention of Astellas's scientific representatives in the crowd.

Astellas wondered whether TruGraf might prove useful in a clinical study to provide a surrogate end point that indicates the relative effectiveness of three different immunosuppressive drugs they were testing. The study's patients would be tested every few months, in the hope that TruGraf would provide signs of immune activation appearing sooner or later in one patient group versus another. If successful, TruGraf could dramatically reduce the time and cost of clinical trials. And if the drug were ever approved, TruGraf might be used as a "companion diagnostic" test to indicate whether a patient was being effectively treated.

We had never considered this idea, but it provided an enormous opportunity to generate early revenue and train the fifty major US transplant programs participating in the study how to use TruGraf, with no marketing expense at all! Of course it took half a year to negotiate the contract, but bringing Roy on as chief medical officer sealed the deal, as it gave Astellas enormous comfort in this new little start-up. If, a few years later, the idea really worked as envisioned, this could be a gold mine—although we certainly couldn't count on it.

EUROFINS ACQUISITION

By early 2016 the marketplace for posttransplant surveillance was heating up. We now had several competitors that were better financed and making a lot of noise, despite their fundamentally flawed data. It was disappointing to see how easily physicians could be swayed by marketing, sales, corporate funding, and grant awards, even when the data did not support much if any utility to using these alternative tests. Of course the companies promoted their products as if they were amazing technological breakthroughs. It was all very Trumpian in nature, seeing as these tests without any utility for monitoring stable patients were being promoted as the ideal solution for just that. In retrospect this approach was consistent with a lot of messaging in the world in 2016. The big question now was whether we would fare better than others in fighting off a massive disinformation campaign in a posttruth world.

As if the situation wasn't challenging enough, we'd soon learn that my partner and cofounder, Dan Salomon, was battling colon cancer. Being relatively young at sixty and an avid surfer in great shape, you can imagine how shocked we were. For more than a year Dan waged a heroic battle against the cancer as he underwent chemotherapy and experimental drug treatments. Maintaining an upbeat and optimistic attitude the entire time, refusing to give in, he somehow summoned the strength to continue his research, care for his patients, and work on refining TruGraf for commercial use. When things got really bad and he couldn't stand, he directed his team over the phone from bed.

Dan's battle with cancer came to an end in November 2016. Many of us got together for a touching service to honor and celebrate his life. As we gathered on the cliffs in Del Mar, California, to share memories and pay our respects, a group of Dan's surfing buddies carried his ashes out to sea in a ceremony known as a paddle-out. They formed a circle, shared their thoughts, and then spread Dan's ashes over the rolling waves of the Pacific Ocean under a spectacular orange, yellow, and purple sunset. It was a devastating blow. We'd lost a friend, a business partner, and a scientific giant in the world of transplant medicine.

Mike stepped up to take on the leadership role for TGI's clinical and scientific programs, acting as an unofficial mentor for the remaining staff and consultants at Scripps who had been working for his best friend. We decided to use Dan's latest TruGraf algorithm as the test we would take to market and made sure our studies and publications supporting reimbursement used this version. We also made a pact to honor Dan's legacy by seeing this through and getting a test into the clinic that helped improve and extend the lives of kidney transplant patients.

As if all this was not challenging enough, we spent nearly all of 2016 operating with very little cash on hand. We desperately needed to raise more money, but that would be extremely difficult until we achieved some more milestones. In March 2016, with our development program handicapped by Dan's illness and several key potential partnerships in negotiation but not yet over the finish line, we had to make one of the most difficult decisions of my career. We had to ask many of our employees to participate in a furlough program under which they reduced their time commitment and compensation while continuing to be employed by the company. If they agreed to stick with us, and if we could raise more money, they would get a bonus a year later that would provide a nice return on their "investment." Agreeing to participate in the program took a great deal of faith in the company.

Some had difficult discussions with their families and concluded it was too risky a career move, or they simply couldn't afford to participate. We lost a few employees immediately, and a few more over time, but we couldn't avoid this path. To survive, we had to find a way to burn less cash each month. Hopefully we would complete a financing deal before losing too many employees or running out of money.

Though venture investors viewed the MDx sector as toxic, we had admirably drummed up interest from high-net-worth individuals, family offices, and strategic investors. Nonetheless, they all wanted us to meet several key milestones before agreeing to invest further. We needed to show the results of independent, external clinical validation studies confirming that our test worked as well as the initial discovery studies indicated. We needed to show progress toward securing a reimbursement decision with CMS. We needed at least one partner with a big presence in the field of transplant medicine to lend more credibility to our technological approach and commercial plans. Our senior team was laser focused on addressing all these points.

Our big breakthrough came in mid-2016 when I received an unsolicited inquiry from Keith Stewart, who was leading the Mayo Clinic's Center for Individualized Medicine. Mayo had established the group with the intent of showcasing how novel approaches to personalized medicine could be applied to benefit patients across the entire Mayo Clinic system, which included hospitals in Minnesota, Arizona, and Florida. One of our early collaborators and scientific advisors was Ray Heilman, a transplant nephrologist at Mayo Arizona, who proposed to Keith that an ideal case study would be the use of our TruGraf blood test applied to surveillance of kidney transplant recipients. Keith and his colleagues were intrigued by the idea and proposed a partnership that involved an investment from Mayo into TGI, a large-scale multiyear study of TruGraf on patients being treated in all three of Mayo's transplant programs, and a related technology development and licensing agreement. This represented an incredible opportunity for TGI and was instrumental in enabling us to emerge from the challenges we had been facing.

With the help of Roy, Courtney, and Darren—who were now working part time on furlough—and our clinical lab employees, who had been kept employed full time in Pleasanton, we were able to initiate collaborative studies with Mayo, complete the ongoing clinical studies needed to support our application for Medicare coverage, and get the CLIA lab operation properly validated and certified. By year's end, the TGI story was much brighter, and we could see a clear path to the clinic, but we had yet to close on the next significant round of financing. The good news encouraged investors, but it was difficult getting anyone to step up with a term sheet to lead and price a round of equity financing. What's more, we had convertible notes coming due. Not only did we need money to support our operations, but we had to settle our past debt, preferably by converting that debt into equity. Such a conversion would occur only if we completed a round of equity financing.

Less than two months after Dan's service in Del Mar, I returned to California in January 2017 with roughly two dozen meetings scheduled over a three-day period at the annual J.P. Morgan Healthcare Conference in San Francisco. On the second morning, I met one of our key investors, Jay Venkatesan, over breakfast at Sears Fine Food on Powell Street. Sitting in the classic breakfast joint, with power meetings going on at every table, Jay scribbled on a napkin the terms under which he would lead a series B equity financing round, and in the process convert all outstanding debt to equity. This would not only provide the additional funding we needed but would also allow us to end the furlough program and clean up our equity structure and associated capitalization table, which would help us in future partnering and financing discussions. I immediately offered to participate and began canvassing our existing investors to solicit others.

It was a huge relief when we completed the series B investment round, but we were not out of the woods yet. By now we realized that to be competitive, we needed to get to market, which meant accelerating our path to reimbursement, which required more money and a larger commercial team. We had lost a year in development compared with our prior plans, and now had several better-financed competitors. We simply didn't have the time to build a commercial team on our own. We needed to be acquired, ideally by a company that shared our vision, appreciated the value of what we had created to date, and had the resources necessary to drive our tests into the clinic.

We knew we needed the help of an investment banker. The big banks were ready to assist, but we worried the deal size might be too small to keep them engaged if the going got tough. Frank Witney from Affymetrix once again came to our aid, recommending we work with a small boutique investment bank in Denver called Evergreen M&A, led by Tod White, a longtime friend and associate of Frank's. Under Tod's leadership, Evergreen became an integral part of our team. Tod and I clicked immediately and would go on to become close collaborators and good friends.

With Tod's help we were able to enter serious discussions with multiple companies about potential deals with a variety of structures, but none of the early offers looked attractive enough. The obvious problem was that we did not have a reimbursement decision and thus could not yet show traction in test adoption by customers. This ramped up the pressure I felt not to let down my investors and my fear of failing to achieve our goals.

Daily I thought about those who had put their money and faith in me to get us to a successful outcome and how they might lose their money or make unsatisfactory returns. Most were personal friends. My high school buddy Andy, with whom I had shared a Boston apartment when I was trying to find my first research job, was an investor. So was my best friend from the Virgin Islands, Captain Loren. What I had imagined might be the crowning achievement of my career, benefiting my own health and thousands of others like me, had the distinct possibility of being a major flop. I never worked harder or under more stress, which probably wasn't good for my transplanted kidney. My transplant nephrologist kept urging me to slow down, but I had to see it through. That old West Indian saying kept popping up in my head. Can't tame a mongoose.

I was now working eighteen-hour days, traveling nationwide to meetings with multiple parties, and engaging with groups on three continents at all hours. Discussions had moved along with four different groups, and we tried our best to see how far we could push each one. They were all aware that multiple bidders were at the table, but they also each had their own strategic objectives and financial bottom lines. It was beginning to appear as if we had reached the end of the road and would have to sell at a price that was not going to make my investors happy. I vividly recall one particularly frustrating call that dragged on for hours without reaching a satisfactory resolution and left me drained and hungry as I had missed dinner. I decided to take a break and drive to the local grocery store.

Then, just as I pulled into a parking spot, with the Grateful Dead still playing in the car, my phone rang. It was Tod calling. He had a potential lifeline for us. A Chinese company he'd recently met that had a strategic interest in renal care was willing to lead a $5 million round to get us over the hump. The only catch was that they also wanted rights to sell our products in China. This could be a risky move given the current political climate. There were active discussions underway in the US Senate about prohibiting Chinese investment in US companies. On the other hand, this might be a deal we could conclude quickly and that would provide us with enough cash to accomplish some of the milestones we needed to uncap our valuation.

As soon as I hung up with Tod, I started calling our other board members. I explained the benefits, risks, and alternatives we were facing. We decided to take the money. Similar to my deal with Takara at GMS twenty years earlier, we'd happily take money now in exchange for rights to sell our services in a territory we could never envision addressing on our own. As far as the risk of government intervention was concerned, we concluded it was highly unlikely that the US Senate could agree to do anything quickly. Even if they ultimately stopped future investment by Chinese companies, the chance they could do this before we closed the deal was near zero.

This was a pivotal turning point. Over the following year we were able to use the funds raised from our Chinese partner to generate data and publications from larger clinical studies that were required for a reimbursement decision from CMS. We used sponsored studies under an early access program to generate obvious and substantial customer interest in our test. By the end of the year, multiple potential buyers were knocking on our door, and they weren't offering bargain basement prices. They were serious, and they knew we were too.

We ultimately wound up selling TGI to Eurofins, closing the deal in late May 2019. A public company traded on the Paris stock exchange and based in Luxembourg, Eurofins is a global conglomerate employing over sixty thousand people across nearly nine hundred different laboratory service businesses in sixty-one countries. In the US, one of their primary areas of focus is clinical diagnostics, and within that business segment they were particularly active in various aspects of infectious disease and transplant diagnostics. Founder, CEO, and major shareholder Gilles Martin was particularly excited about the prospects for our business and ultimately presented an offer we couldn't pass up.

In an ironic twist of events similar to what had happened during the sale of GMS to Affymetrix, Elise and I had a long-planned vacation scheduled just as we were trying to complete negotiations with Eurofins. This time we were on a cruise to Cuba. The last points of discussion were agreed upon while Elise and I were on a yacht moored in the harbor in Santiago de Cuba, with me participating via satellite phone connection. When the deal was finally done, I went out on the balcony overlooking the city where Fidel Castro had launched his revolution and celebrated with a tall glass of Santiago's finest rum.

TruGraf went on to receive CMS coverage in November 2019. Kidney transplant patients are now able to use TruGraf tests to rule out silent subclinical rejection, in lieu of surveillance biopsies. All our investors made money on the deal. More importantly, they contributed to bringing a novel biomarker test to the clinic, one that has the potential to change the standard of care for kidney transplant recipients and extend the lives of hundreds of thousands of patients.

This last point is particularly important to the field of transplant medicine given the severe organ donor shortage relative to the number of those in need. It was also important to me, a kidney recipient who wanted his graft to function as long as possible. This venture was never about the money. Our mission was to help people like me live longer, healthier, happier lives, and the prospect of making money on the business was just the carrot to raise the financing necessary to pursue our quest.

Two months later, in January 2020, I was watching the six o'clock news one evening when a report appeared about a plane en route to the US from China carrying several sick passengers. They had apparently been infected with some unknown virus. I texted my high school friend Andy, now a rocket scientist with Pratt & Whitney and a lifelong science junkie.

"Did you see the news about that plane with sick people from China?" I wrote. "In case you ever wondered, this is what a bioterrorist attack would look like." Although such a scenario was conceivable, I didn't really believe it was a terrorist attack, and followed the text with a phone call to talk about this in more detail—but I remembered the exchange clearly.

I was supposed to attend a meeting in Europe later that month. I thought to myself, "Do I really want to go meet with several hundred people from all over the world when it's the height of flu season and there's some strange new virus in the news too?" I canceled my travel plans. Transplant Genomics had already been sold, and though I was staying on to help ensure a successful transition for Eurofins, at some point I needed to stop pushing so hard. I was, after all, an immunocompromised transplant recipient. To slow down was just prudent.

A week or so later, Elise and I flew to St. Thomas on our way to a quiet week alone back on St. John. We met our old friend Jeff James at the airport. Jeff had retired from the taxi business after Hurricanes Irma and Maria devastated the USVI in September 2017, effectively shutting down tourism for more than a year. He still gave us a ride to Red Hook for old time's sake, and we reflected on the past twenty years.

We boarded the ferry, and as we motored out of the harbor, I stared over the railing down at the crystal-clear turquoise water, getting lost in its beautiful shades of blue. I looked up and counted off the cays to the north. Thatch, Grassy, Mingo, Lovongo, and Congo. I was in a trance, hypnotized by the beauty of this place and flooded with memories of some of the best years of my life.

For the next ten days we stayed at Estate Rose, our former home on St. John (which we'd sold in 2015) and went back in time. We mostly hung around the house, hosted visitors daily, made trips to see friends at their homes or places of work, and of course set aside time for daily adventures out in the national park. It was a blissful week. There's a part of St. John that touched my soul and will never leave, and it felt wonderful to reengage.

No more than two or three days after returning home, several physicians called to warn me about a new virus that caused a disease that would come to be named COVID-19. Very little was known other than that it was a novel coronavirus that could be deadly for people with compromised immune systems. There was no treatment and no vaccine. I was told that I should prepare to lock down at home indefinitely. It literally could be years.

Within days I notified my superiors that I would be stepping down as CEO of Eurofins-TGI since there was no way I could continue to serve in that role under these circumstances. Besides, I didn't want to spend whatever remaining time I might have working for a large company. It was probably exactly the right time for me to step back from work and enjoy life anyway. Or perhaps just time for another break before seeking life's next adventure. Good thing I had plenty of experience dealing with unexpected events!

In the end, TGI turned out to be yet another successful venture. It took longer than we had hoped to go from concept to an approved and reimbursed clinical diagnostic test, but we did it. We accomplished what we set out to do, taking an idea for a diagnostic marker and making it into a reimbursed test used in transplant centers as part of a strategy to extend the lives of grafts and patients. Not many people can say that. What's more, all investors made money, so they were happy with the risk they took and proud of the accomplishment their funding enabled.

We did good. We had the kind of impact on the practice of medicine that all of us had envisioned from the start. There were many twists and turns, and there was a lot of stress, hard work, and creative thinking. We responded as best as we could when confronted with unexpected events. It took an incredible degree of focus, determination, persistence, creativity, and resilience. We pursued it with passion and leveraged our collective skills and the many relationships we had developed over the years. As the Beatles famously put it, we got by with a little help from our friends. At the end of the day, there was a sense of personal fulfillment that I believe was felt by every member of the team. I know I felt it, and that feeling is worth more than whatever amount of financial gain there may have been.

AFTERWORD

All companies begin with a vision. Individuals or partners develop some sort of plan and iterate as new information arises. It takes an enormous amount of their time, forces them to commit, and requires some degree of funding. If sophisticated investors are involved, the plan is undoubtedly subjected to intensive due diligence. Models are developed, scrutinized, and refined. Yet despite this hard work, which often involves smart people with significant experience, it's been estimated that 90 percent of technology-based ventures do not survive past five years. Some fail for a host of strategic or operational shortcomings addressed in any decent business school course. Others fail because, no matter their degree of planning or vetting, they are unable to adequately address unexpected events.

Nassim Nicholas Taleb has written extensively of black swan events—rare, outlying occurrences that have unusually large impacts. The stories I've shared in this book do not highlight such outliers but rather what I call *inevitable unexpected events*. Things you never saw coming, that you never planned for, but which occur with relatively high frequency. I can't predict what they may be or when they may occur. Nobody can. But I can almost guarantee you will encounter them. Over the course of five years, these events will occur frequently enough that one's ability to address them well will likely determine the difference between a business's success and failure. Any wrong move can take you down.

These unexpected events may present in the form of barriers to overcome. Or they may present as opportunities worthy of addressing, but you need to decide whether to do so. They are not exclusively business issues, although they are all issues that will affect your business. I've tried to illustrate this with examples drawn from nearly forty years of working with scientists and clinicians to transform inventions into successful commercial products.

We encounter these inevitable unexpected events regardless of our collective intelligence and experience, the models we develop, or the plans we base on those models. The unknown is humbling, but it reminds us of the incredible complexity and beauty of biology, life, and the universe we inhabit. The number of factors one would need to have considered, accounted for, and correctly predicted to have a "perfect plan" is comparable to the number of stars in the sky.

This doesn't mean we're doomed to failure. The likelihood of making beneficial decisions when facing the unexpected, however, is increased by the routine practice of certain values, skills, and approaches. These unexpected events should not be feared but rather appreciated as opportunities to flourish and to distinguish yourself in the eyes of customers, competitors, partners, and investors.

I've purposely avoided presenting my thoughts as a how-to guide, as I don't believe there is a single formula that applies to every situation one may encounter. Having said that, some of the practices that have been particularly helpful to me with respect to navigating life's inevitable unexpected events include the following:

- Develop strong foundations, with deep knowledge and experience in your domain.
- Develop living plans that are regularly updated.
- Respect the unknown, and expect unanticipated events.
- Assemble diverse teams with complementary skills.
- Establish a culture where people can thrive and have fun.
- Act in a calm, focused, efficient, and timely manner.
- Be persistent yet adaptable, open minded, flexible, and resilient.
- Always be building and leveraging resources and relationships.
- Always be thinking about options.

This list isn't meant to be comprehensive, but it has served me well. As with any other skill set, awareness can be generated, but there will still be a spectrum of performance across individuals regarding how well they are able to apply these values and approaches to their own businesses. Certain values and approaches I've described may not resonate as well for some as for others.

My guidance is not about storing a list in your memory and pulling certain items out when needed. It's more about developing a practice, a way of conducting business (or your life). If you are following them all the time, you will be as prepared as possible when confronting life's inevitable unexpected events.

I hope the stories I've shared have been informative, insightful, and perhaps even entertaining and inspiring. The opportunities for today's entrepreneurs can be more exciting and impactful than ever. While this book was written with aspiring bioentrepreneurs in mind, I believe what I've shared will be helpful to anyone pursuing a creative endeavor, regardless of your field of interest. With a healthy respect for the unknown and unexpected, and proper preparation and execution, there is an opportunity to achieve great things and have a lot of fun doing so.

ACKNOWLEDGMENTS

First and foremost, I'd like to thank my wife, Elise, for support, encouragement, helpful commentary, and editing throughout this project. I thank Andrew Diamond for planting the seed of an idea for this book and always having an inspirational thought or a lighthearted joke to share. I'm grateful to all my family, friends, and professional colleagues for their contributions to the events that shaped my life, whether or not your names are mentioned here. I'm also grateful to all of the committed and talented physicians and related caregivers who helped keep me in good health throughout.

I thank the following people for valuable contributions to this work. Scott Allan and the rest of the team at SPS for helping me learn the process of book writing and publishing. Jennifer Bradshaw for helpful developmental editing, especially in the early stages when my manuscript was very rough and twice as long. J. Fenton Williams, Andrew DeBiccari, Loren Nickbarg, Courtney Schieve, Melissa Lorusso, Riccardo Pigliucci, and Roy First for their helpful input on various sections of the manuscript. Lena Chow for helping me think through the various paths forward that I might have chosen for this book and her helpful commentary on the entire draft manuscript. Karen McNally Upson, Mari Kesselring, Adria Batt, and their colleagues at Girl Friday Productions for their perspectives and assistance in publishing this book and getting the attention of my desired audience. Matthew Patin for major contributions in the form of developmental and line editing. Mona Houck at Miller Korzenik Sommers Rayman LLP for legal review and contracting.

ABOUT THE AUTHOR

 Dr. Stan Rose is a biologist and serial entrepreneur. He received his BA from Cornell University and his PhD from the Massachusetts Institute of Technology. Dr. Rose has spent over three decades working with leading scientists and clinicians to create substantial commercial value from inventions related to DNA and genome analysis. During that time, he has raised more than $100 million in financing and led businesses to create more than $1 billion in market value by enabling advances in biological research, diagnostics, and therapeutics. The products of these businesses have positively affected millions of lives, and some have been used to save and extend his own.

Dr. Rose continues to advise and direct early-stage companies developing innovative, high-impact life science products and services through Rose Ventures Inc. You can learn more about his company at roseventures.net.

Made in United States
North Haven, CT
15 January 2025

64448319R00174